PREFACE

This manual supplements the text *Statistics for Business and Economics*, Seventh Edition, by Jim McClave, P. George Benson, and Terry Sincich (Prentice Hall. Inc., 1998). It provides detailed explanations for how to use Microsoft Excel97® (version 8.0) to run many of the statistical analyses presented in the text. Examples from *Statistics for Business and Economics*, 7/e, are used throughout this manual and page references are given so that the student may easily find the corresponding Excel material when working through the text.

This manual assumes that students have little or no experience working with Excel. Consequently, the manual begins with a Primer that introduces Excel basics needed for statistical analysis of data. The Primer provides the basic knowledge one needs to navigate in Excel. Experienced Excel users may choose to skip this material and begin with the core chapters.

Chapters 1-18 are correlated directly with the chapters in *Statistics for Business and Economics*, 7/e. Each chapter in the manual begins with a brief introduction that states the topics covered in the text and gives a brief description of the procedures available for use in Excel. A table indicating which examples from the text are solved in the Manual, with corresponding pages, is then provided. The remaining sections within each chapter give specific instruction on how to use Excel to conduct the pertinent statistical analysis presented in the text. By comparing their generated Excel output to the output shown in *Statistics for Business and Economics*, 7/e and working through the "how-to" steps, students will gain confidence in their ability to use Excel to analyze data. They will also gain sufficient knowledge of Excel to solve many of the homework problems with the techniques learned in the chapter examples.

To make it as easy as possible to do the homework problems in the text, all of the files found on the ASCII data disk packaged in the back of each copy of *Statistics for Business and Economics*, 7/e have been converted to Excel Workbooks. They are available on a ftp site for download. To access them, the user should visit the McClave web site at www.prenhall.com/mcclave and click on the *Statistics for Business and Economics*, 7/e book.

My approach to using Excel for statistical analysis is to make the Excel portion of the analysis as simple as possible for the student. The statistical concepts and techniques being presented in the text are challenging enough for the typical student without compounding the problem by using a software package that will provide more confusion. Consequently, I present screen captures of the Excel menus and windows where possible. These screen captures present the actual Excel menus that will be used in the analysis of the data. In this manual, I have chosen to present only those techniques that are provided in the standard "off-the-shelf" Excel. In the future, an Excel add-on will be available to augment the standard Excel features. Check the McClave website for additional information.

I would like to thank Beverly Dretzke and Kenneth Heilman for their permission to use the material presented in the Primer which is borrowed extensively from their text, *Statistics with Microsoft Excel* (Prentice Hall Inc., 1997). In just thirty pages, they do an outstanding job of introducing the basic information one needs to work effectively in Excel. I must also thank my "Excel Dream Team" of Melanie Feldman, Lyndi Mulder, and Christine Wilson. They produced the Excel output for all of the chapter examples and converted the ASCII files into Excel Workbooks. Thanks are due to Ann Heath and Mindy McClard at Prentice Hall who always provided the support and resources that I needed to finish this work. And finally, a special thanks to my wife, Ashlie, who not only supports my work, but puts up with me as deadlines approach.

Mark Dummeldinger
University of South Florida
Tampa, Florida

THE MICROSOFT® EXCEL
SUPPLEMENT
MARK DUMMELDINGER

STATISTICS
FOR **BUSINESS**
AND **ECONOMICS**
SEVENTH EDITION

McCLAVE • BENSON • SINCICH

PRENTICE HALL, Upper Saddle River, NJ 07458

Executive Editor: *Ann Heath*
Special Projects Manager: *Barbara A. Murray*
Production Editor: *Dawn Blayer*
Production Coordinator: *Alan Fischer*
Supplement Cover Manager: *Paul Gourhan*
Editorial Assistant: *Mindy McClard*

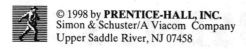

© 1998 by **PRENTICE-HALL, INC.**
Simon & Schuster/A Viacom Company
Upper Saddle River, NJ 07458

Printed in the United States of America

10 9 8 7 6 5 4 3 2 1

ISBN 0-13-080907-1

Prentice-Hall International (UK) Limited, *London*
Prentice-Hall of Australia Pty. Limited, *Sydney*
Prentice-Hall Canada, Inc., *Toronto*
Prentice-Hall Hispanoamericana, S.A., *Mexico*
Prentice-Hall of India Private Limited, *New Delhi*
Prentice-Hall of Japan, Inc., *Tokyo*
Simon & Schuster Asia Pte. Ltd., *Singapore*
Editora Prentice-Hall do Brasil, Ltda., *Rio de Janeiro*

CONTENTS

Excel Basics Needed for Statistical Analysis of Data

P. 1 Introduction and Overview

This manual is designed for use with McClave, Benson, and Sincich *Statistics for Business and Economics*, 7th edition. It is not intended to take the place of your Excel user's manual, however it will introduce the Excel novice to the software and provide the basic tools necessary to analyze statistical data using Excel. To accomplish this goal, we use a three-part process. First, we introduce the statistical procedures available in Excel. Next, we illustrate these procedures by teaching you how to perform the Excel commands required to produce the output from selected examples in *Statistics for Business and Economics 7/e*. Both the steps taken and output generated are provided in this manual to teach you the Excel steps to be followed.. The final part of our process is to provide you with Excel data sets that may be used to complete homework exercises in the McClave/Benson/Sincich text. Our hope is that this "introduce-learn-practice" format will enable you to finish the course with a firm understanding of how Excel can be used to analyze statistical data.

We believe that the Excel portion of a statistics course should serve strictly to enhance the statistics that is being taught. We have tried to keep this philosophy in mind when writing this manual. We have attempted to provide an easy-to-use format that will allow you to use Excel to calculate the statistics you learn in class. If we have been successful, you will view Excel as valuable tool for the statistician. Used correctly, Excel allows the statistician to spend more time using, and less time calculating, the kind of information that you will explore in your statistics course.

P.1. 1 Versions of Excel

This manual principally uses Excel 97 (version 8.0). Many different versions of Excel exist; Excel 97 is the most current at the time of this writing. All of the versions function in essentially the same way, whether used on the PC or a Mac, but you will notice slight differences in how the screens look and in the names of some commands. In this manual, we only use statistical tools that are available in the "off-the-shelf" version of Excel. No macros or other extensive programming of Excel will be discussed in this manual. See your Excel user's manual if you would like more information about these issues.

P.1.2 Versions of Windows

The copies of screens shown in this book are taken from a PC using Windows 95. They will appear slightly different if using Windows 3.x or a Mac operating under System 7. After you are operating comfortably within Excel, these differences should be minor. There will, however, be slight differences between Macs and PCs in the keys used for commands.

P.1.3 What may be skipped

If you have used spreadsheets before, you can probably omit much of the first chapter. Other programs, such as Lotus 1-2-3 and Quattro, use slightly different terminology when describing the. The concepts, however, are essentially the same although the terms and/or procedures may differ slightly.

- For those of you who are looking for commands for a specific procedure or example from *Statistics for Business and Economics*, 7/e you will find that each of the chapters may be used independently.

P.1.4   More detailed information on Excel

A glance at the bookshelves in the computer section of most bookstores will reveal a number of books that deal with Excel in all its various versions. Few deal with Excel as a way to perform statistical analyses.

Books we have referred to when preparing this manual include the following:

Dretzke, B., & Heilman, K. (1998) . *Statistics with Microsoft® Excel.* Upper Saddle River, NJ. Prentice Hall

Gold, L. & Post, D. (1995). *The Complete Idiot's Guide to Excel for Windows 95*. Indianapolis, IN: Que.

Halvorson, M. & Young, M. (1997). *Running Microsoft Office 97*. Redmond, WA: Microsoft Press.

Marmel, E., Bucki, L., & Guilford, E. (1995). *The Big Basics book of Excel for Windows 95.* Indianapolis, IN: Que.

Microsoft Corporation (1994). *User's Guide. Microsoft Excel*. Redmond, WA: Microsoft Press.

Nelson, S. L. (1966). *Microsoft Excel 97 Field Guide*. Redmond, WA: Microsoft Press.

Neufeld, J. L. (1997). *Learning Business Statistics with Microsoft Excel*. Upper Saddle River, NJ: Prentice Hall.

Nicholson, J. R. & Nicholson, S. R. (1997). *Discover Excel 97*. Foster City, CA: IDG Books.

P.2 What You Need to know to Begin Using Excel

P.2.1 Using the mouse

Mice come in several forms. The majority are provided with new computers and roll on the desktop or pad. A small ball on the bottom, when rolled, causes the pointer on the screen (called the **screen pointer**) to move in a corresponding way. Another version (called a trackball) places a larger ball in a framework that allows you to roll the ball with your fingers. Finally, there are other forms that have small screens that you move your finger across as you would move the mouse. The pressure of your finger moving across the screen causes a screen pointer to move in synchrony with your movements.

All devices have at least one, and most likely two or more, buttons that you can click or hold down, sometimes while also moving the ball. There are four basic actions you will need to use in operating the mouse:

- **Point** You point to objects on the screen by sliding the mouse on the deskpad or rolling the trackball. The screen pointer will track the movements made on your desk. The shape of the screen pointer will change, most often being an outline arrow or the outline of a plus sign when using Excel, but changing with the task to be done.

- **Click** "Click" means to press and release the left mouse button (called a left-click). If you are pointing at an executable command, this action will cause it to take place. If you point to any cell on the spreadsheet and click, that cell becomes the **active cell** and is ready to receive data. Sometimes you may be asked to press and release the right mouse button (called a right-click), which is commonly used to place a shortcut menu on the screen. The above assumes you are using the settings for the mouse provided by the manufacturer with your right hand. If you are left-handed or want to reverse the way the buttons function, this can be done. Click on the **Help** icon above the **Start** button on the Windows 95 screen and look for *mouse, buttons, reversing* in the **Index**.

• **Double-click** "Double-click" means to press and release the left mouse button twice rapidly. If you fail to press rapidly enough, it is interpreted as one click. Often this process replaces the two-step sequence of selecting a command and then clicking on **OK** to execute that command.

• **Drag.** Objects on the screen are moved by dragging. To drag, place the mouse pointer on the item you want to move, click and hold the left mouse button --- do NOT release it. While you hold the mouse button down, slide the mouse to move the screen pointer and the item to the location you want. Then release the mouse button.

P.2.2 Starting and exiting Excel

To start the program using either Windows 95 or 3.11:

Windows 95: Click on **Start** in the lower left of the screen. Move the mouse to **Programs** and then continue moving through menus until you find the **Microsoft** Excel icon to click and begin.

If you have Office 95 or Office 97, you may have to find the folder containing that suite, open it, and double-click on the icon of the Excel program you find there.

You may want to go through the Quick Preview online tutorial if you are unfamiliar with spreadsheets and need a quick overview. This is often found in the Excel folder.

Windows 3.x: In the **Program Manager**, locate the icon or folder containing the Excel icon. Double-click on it to begin.

To exit the program using either Windows 95 or 3.11:

Windows 95: Click in the upper **X** (the **close button**) that you find in the upper right corner of the screen. (If two sets of boxes are showing, the lower set applies to the worksheet (spreadsheet) you have showing while the upper one is for the application or program itself, (i.e., Excel). If you have edited (changed) any of the information in the **workbook**, you will be prompted to save the information before closing the program. In many computer labs, you may be asked to save all of your data on a diskette. We will describe this procedure later.

Windows 3.x: Use the same procedure as above. The **X** is a general sign to indicate you want to stop using or to exit a program. You can also select **Exit** from the **File** menu for either Windows 95 or Windows 3.x.

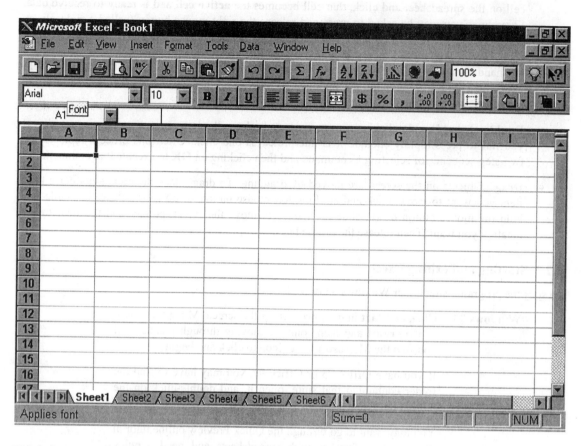

P.2.3 Layout of worksheets and workbooks

The above figure shows what is on the screen when version 7 of Excel is opened. It may be slightly different from what you have on your screen. The list that follows briefly describes each of the items on the figure above, starting at the top.

- **Program Title Bar** This is most likely at the very top of the screen, with the default title being Microsoft Excel - Book 1. It indicates the name of the application and the fact that you are in what is called *Book 1*, the name given to a newly opened spreadsheet. Each book initially consists of 16 worksheets (this can be changed) which are stored together as a unit called a book. When you save your work, all of the sheets in this book will be saved together as one file.

- **Program Icons** Known as **sizing buttons** in Office 97, these are at the very right on the Program Title Bar, just as on the screen shown above. There are three program icons. Each is described below.

  - The **minimize button** "shrinks" the program which is then represented as a button on the **taskbar** at the bottom of the screen. This is part of Windows 95, which inactivates, but does not close, programs and places their icon at the bottom of the screen so they can be immediately reactivated.

  - The **maximize button** switches (toggles) between the full-screen and window views.

- ☒ The **close button**, which closes the Excel application. You will be asked if you want to save your work, if there is any, before the application is closed.

- **Main menu bar**. Commands are grouped into categories such as *File, Edit, View,* etc. Clicking on one of these will drop down the commands in that group. Those that are useful for our purposes will be discussed later.

- **Workbook Icons**. These are the same as the **program icons** described above, except that they apply to the specific workbook being used rather than to the program.

- **Standard Toolbar**. This is a ribbon of icons that are designed to ease your access to commands. Some are not as obvious as one might wish, but all you need to do to find out what the button does is to point at it with your mouse pointer and pause. Its name is then displayed. For example, the first icon, labeled **New**, resembles a sheet of paper and will create a new workbook if it is clicked. The second will open a file, etc. You can already see how there are a number of ways to execute the same command. Near the extreme right of the toolbar we have the **Tip Wizard** (like a light bulb) which will give us information about how to do something more effectively. Click on it and you will see a general tip inserted in a space between the **Formatting Toolbar** and the **Formula Bar**. Click again to remove it. Next to Tip Wizard is another form of *Help*, the **Help Tool**. If you click on that button, the screen pointer changes to a question mark. Move it to the part of the screen you need to know more about, click the mouse, and it will give you a list of topics to explain the specific question you have. Try it by clicking on it and then moving to the letters at the top of each column. You will be given a list of *Parts of the Microsoft Excel Screen* that you can choose from for a brief explanation of their purpose. Click on *Column Heading* and you will be given a brief explanation and more options, such as adjusting column width, hiding a row or column, etc.

- **Formatting Toolbar**. Commands that change the appearance of your text are found here. First, you have the default font listed, *Arial* in most cases. If you wish to use a different font you need only click on the down arrow next to the font box to see which ones are available. To change the default font for the whole spreadsheet, use **Help** and search for the term *fonts*. Click on the second option to obtain a *How To* box with directions for changing the default startup workbook or the standard font.

The size of the font (10) is displayed in the next window with an arrow for changing it.

Following this are buttons for **bold**, *italic*, underline, left-alignment, center-alignment, and centering across columns. The next five icons control the form of currency, percentage, use of commas in numbers, and the number of decimals displayed. To place any of a variety of borders around a cell or cells, use the next icon. The last two deal with colors, which we will not cover.

- **Formula Bar**. The first window shows the address of the active cell in the worksheet that is displayed. Initially it is A1, so this is the address displayed. Move to a different cell and click on it to make it the active cell. Now that cell's address is displayed.

This first box on the formula bar is also called the **Name Box**. To learn how to use it, click on *Help* on the Main Menu Bar, then *Search for Help on ...*, and type in *name box* followed by clicking on *Display*. You will have an explanation of how to name a cell, formula, or range of cells.

Notice what happens to the Formula Bar when we type some numbers in cell A1. Three more buttons appear:

- The red X is clicked when we want to "destroy" or delete the information we have typed in the active cell. That information is also displayed in the Formula Bar and will be removed from both sites if we click on the X.

- The green check mark, when clicked, indicates that the data as entered are acceptable. The data will remain in the cell, but the three buttons disappear, indicating that the cell is not being edited.

- Finally, the f_x is an icon to turn on the **Function Wizard**, a set of over 300 functions in categories such as Financial, Math & Trig, Statistical, etc. We will use the statistical functions quite often, and discuss the use of this tool throughout the chapters.

- **Worksheet Area**. Finally, we have the worksheet, which consists of 4,194,304 cells with columns labeled as letters and rows as numbers. There are 256 columns and 16,384 rows. Press CTRL+DOWN ARROW (at the same time) to move to the last row and CTRL+RIGHT ARROW to move to the last column. Each cell is identified by the combination of its column letter and row number, as is displayed in the Name Box.

16380						
16381						
16382						
16383						
16384					This is row 16,384 and column IV	

Sheet1 / Sheet2 / Sheet3 / Sheet4 / Sheet5 / Sheet6

Ready   Sum=0   NUM

- **Scroll Bars** are found at the right and at the bottom of the worksheet. There are two small arrows, which look like a triangle laid on its side at either end of each scrollbar that, when clicked with the mouse, will move the screen up, down, right, or left one line for each press. Some users call the box within the scroll bar an *elevator*. You can grab the box or elevator and drag it. The screen will move a distance that corresponds to the amount you move the box. Finally, if you click in the shaded area between the box and the top or bottom of the scroll bar, the screen will move one whole screen in the direction you click. Thus, you can move a line at a time, a screen at a time, or from the top to the bottom of the screen. If you drag the elevator to the bottom, you will not move to row 16,384 but only down about two screens. If you had data that extended to row 16,384, then the elevator would move to that location. Also, if you hold down the shift key while dragging the box, you can move to the end of the row or column.

- **Worksheet Tabs**. These are at the lower left of the screen and are labeled as *Sheet 1, Sheet 2*, etc. The default setting provides 16 of these tabs, which you can move through by clicking the arrows to the left of the name. Try it. Two arrows will move the active sheet to the left: one moves a sheet at a time and the other will move to the left-most sheet. The same applies to the right arrows. All 16 of these worksheets are stored together as one unit, called a Book.

P.2.4 Menus, toolbars, and dialog boxes

The Windows icon is at the very top of the screen to the left of Microsoft Excel. Use this to restore, minimize, close, etc.

The **Main Menu Bar** is at the top of the Excel screen.. Click on *File* and you will have a set of commands drops down, beginning with *New* and ending with *Exit*. Most of these deal with operations on files. Notice that you can use combinations of keys to execute many of these commands. Key combinations are shown after the name. If you want to open a new file, press **CTRL+N** and you will have a new blank worksheet opened. **CTRL+V** will paste material from the **Clipboard** into the location you specify with the active cell.

Click somewhere on the blank spreadsheet and the dropdown commands will disappear. Now move the mouse pointer to the icons below the words that make up the Main Menu. These icons are on the Workbook Icon Bar. Hold the pointer to the second icon from the left for a moment and you will see the work *Open* appear. Click on that icon and you will open a new worksheet.

Rather than reading our explanation of each command, here is how you can find out what each does: Move the mouse pointer to the up-arrow question mark at the extreme right side of the Workbook Icons. This is called the **Shortcut Help Icon** or **Help Tool**. Click on it. Now the mouse pointer changes to a similar icon on the screen (the arrow is now in outline form). Move the pointer to **Edit** on the **Main Menu Bar**. Click so that you drop down the set of commands. Now click on **Copy**. Microsoft Excel Help now displays this box:

Copy command (Edit menu)

Copies the selection onto the Clipboard.

As you move to higher versions of Excel, the explanations become more elaborate. In Version 8, a longer description is given and some of the phrases are colored green and underlined. If you click on them you will be transferred to another screen that provides more detailed information.

Try clicking on the icon of a light bulb to the left of the Shortcut Help Icon. The Tip Wizard will give you hints on how to do things more efficiently.

The **Status Bar** is at the bottom of the Excel screen. (At the very bottom of the complete screen is the **Taskbar** for Windows 95). The Status Bar indicates what is happening. Most of the time, when nothing special is being done, it simply says *Ready* at the left of the screen. When you are editing a cell (changing information in it) then the word **Edit** will be displayed. Enter a number in cell A1, say 12359. Click the green check mark to accept the entry. The number is displayed in A1 and also in the Formula Bar. The three icons described above also disappear. If we want to change the 5 to a 6, move the pointer to the numbers in the formula bar. Now the pointer changes to an **I**-beam, which you can place just to the right of the 5, before the 9. Do this by clicking in that location. The three icons reappear because you have started to edit the contents of the cell. The word *Edit* is displayed in the Status Bar. Now press the backspace key and the 5 disappears. Enter a 6 and then press the Enter key or click on the check mark to accept the change.

Also shown at the right of the Status Bar is whether the **Number Lock** is turned on so you can use the keypad to enter numbers. Press the **Num Lock** key on the keyboard to turn it on or off. If the **Scroll Lock** is on or the **Caps Lock** keys are on this will also be shown here.

Dialog Boxes usually require that you choose from a number of alternatives. For example, in the **Save As** dialog box shown below, you first must choose the place to save the file. Here we have the A: drive selected as the location. If you click on the arrow to the right, the set of possible locations will be displayed, including the C: drive and any servers that are available. You can then click on your choice to activate it and, if there are currently files of the same type in that location, they will be displayed. Hold the pointer to the icons to the right of the window for their name. A description of their function can be found in the Help file. **File name** is the place where you type the name you wish to use for the file. The default of *Book 2* is shown here. The type of file can be selected in the window below. In most cases, the default shown here is what you will use. Note the numerous options for the format in which a file can be saved when you click on the arrow by the window.

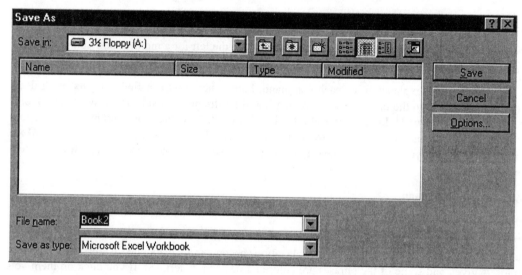

P.2.5 Manipulating Windows

We will discuss moving from one window to another, using the sizing buttons, and changing the size of windows using the mouse pointer.

The name **Windows** aptly describes the major feature of computers today. Excel is described as working within Windows 95. With windows, the user has the ability to have a number of programs or applications operating at the same time and displayed on the screen at the same time. You also have this opportunity within Excel, in that you can move from sheet to sheet within a workbook as well as changing to another workbook.. All windows, as all sheets, are readily available, but only one is active and ready for use at a time. To move from one sheet to another in a workbook, simply click on the Sheet Tab at the bottom of the spreadsheet. As you move to Sheet 5, by clicking on it, Sheet 6 tab appears, and so on until you have moved through 16 sheets. You can also do this one sheet at time with the center arrows to the left of the sheet tabs. Click on the outer two arrows to move to the extreme right (Sheet 16) or extreme left (Sheet 1) of the series in that workbook. Instead of seeing Sheet 1, Sheet 2, etc., you can name these, say as Homework 1, Lab 2, etc. Use your knowledge of the Help option to find out how. As always, we recommend that you use the Shortcut Help Icon to clear up any questions about what different icons are called or how they are used. You may also need to add more sheets, which can be done by using the **Insert - Worksheet** command.

Sizing Buttons were described previously. In both the Excel program and in the Windows program these are displayed at the upper right. The Minimize Button reduces the spreadsheet to a small rectangle and places it near the bottom of the screen. When a spreadsheet has been minimized, a new icon appears, the Restore Button. When clicked on, it will restore the spreadsheet to the size and location it had before being minimized. The Maximize Button enlarges the spreadsheet to fill all available space on the screen. When you have minimized a spreadsheet (or a program in Windows) you have not closed or quit the program. It is still ready to go, but waiting in the wings, so to speak. Finally, the **Close Button** resembles the X seen in the **Formula Bar** when editing data. This commands the program to close the book you are working on. You are then asked if you want to save changes you have made. If you say yes, then you are asked for the name to use in saving the workbook and location for it. Try it. When you have closed a file (Book in this case) you haven't stopped Excel from operating. The toolbars are still there but the Menu Bar now only has *File* and *Help* available. It is expected that you will create a new file or open an existing file

P.3 Ways to get help

We have covered most of the following ways in earlier discussions, but we will review them here and provide a bit more detail than given before.

P .3.1 Help on the Main Menu

The Help command is the rightmost command on the Main Menu Bar. Click on it and you will see a menu providing these options: *Contents*, *Search for Help on ...*, and *Index*. These options may differ slightly with the version of Excel you are using. *Contents* presents broad categories which are broken down into finer sections. *Search* allows you to move through a list of topics and select the one most related to your problem. *Index* presents the topics as you would find them listed in the index at the back of a book. Within each of these you always have the option of moving from one to the other using commands near the top of the screen.

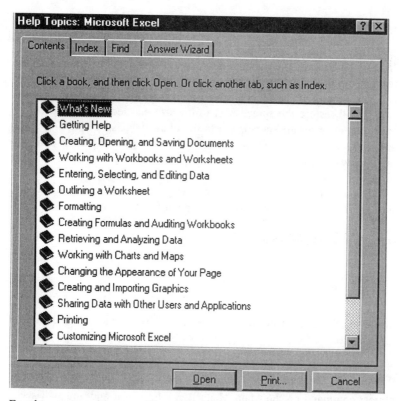

For the person with a specific question, the *Search* option is probably the most useful. You do, however, need to use the terms that the Help database uses. For example, assume that you wanted to change the format of numbers so that there are more or fewer decimals displayed. You begin by typing the word *numbers*, in the window. As you type, the list of terms moves to the word you type, followed by subcategories of that term. If you click *Display*, then more choices are given. Click on the one most related to your problem, and a description of how to deal with it will most likely appear. An example is given at the top of the next page.

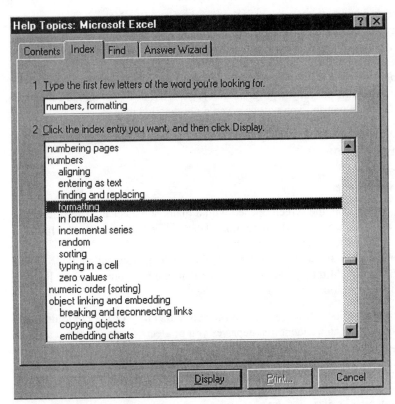

After you click the *Display* key on the above window, a smaller window with a finer breakdown of the topic appears:

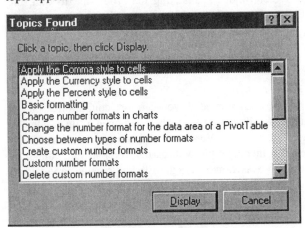

As you scroll down the list and select the appropriate description of the topic you want more information on, you may find that when you ask for help you will have the Answer Wizard window displayed. Instead of giving you written directions, it will give you a series of steps to follow on your spreadsheet that will answer your question.

P.3.2 Answer Wizard

The most recent versions of Excel provide this amusing, active image that will answer your questions. Artificial intelligence technology has been integrated into this feature, so that when you write a question you should get an appropriate response or set of selections that are likely to help you with your problem. It is a *context-sensitive* feature. What you are working on establishes the context, within which the Wizard will search. For example, if you are drawing a chart and need help in labeling the axes, the program recognizes that you are using this part of the program and gives a list of topics that are likely to relate to the question you have. Click on one and you will be given more detailed help.

P.4 Opening and Saving Documents

1.4.1 Opening a brand new spreadsheet

If you started Excel by clicking on the icon, the screen opened with a blank spreadsheet. The title at the top indicates it is called *Book 1* and the tabs across the bottom are labeled *Sheet 1, Sheet 2,* etc. Initially there are 16 sheets available. All sheets together are stored in one unit, called a book. You might, for example, choose to keep all homework assignments for one class in one unit, now called *Book 1*, but renamed by you as *Stats 1 HW*. You could then create other books that contain your personal budget, your records as the treasurer of an organization, and so on.

When you enter information into the worksheet, it is stored in the active memory of the computer, and will disappear if power is lost, whether by an accident that deprives you of electrical power or by turning off the machine without saving your work.

It is wise to save your work often, especially if you are working on a complex project that requires many hours of data entry or processing. Use the automatic save feature. Find directions for using it in **saving documents, protecting work**, in the list of **Help** topics!

If you click on that X in the upper right of the Excel window, indicating that you want to quit, the program will ask you if you want to save the file you have created. If you have already saved it, and therefore have named it, Excel will save it using the same name unless you use the Save As ... command, which is used to change the name or location for saving.

P.4.2 Opening a file you have already created

If you want to continue working on a file that you previously created, you can just double-click on the icon that represents that file. The program will automatically open Excel when you open a file created by Excel. Sometimes this causes a problem if you create a file in Version 7 and want to open it using a computer that only contains Version 5. Files are often incompatible with earlier versions and cannot be opened by an earlier version. One solution is to use **Save As...** and save the file you created in version 7 in the format that can be used by version 5.

P.5 Entering information

In the previous chapter we described the different parts of the screen – the Main Menu Bar, the Program Title Bar, program icons, the Standard Toolbar, the Formatting Toolbar, worksheet tables, Status Bar, and Scroll Bars. We also showed the various shapes that the mouse pointer can take. Now we are ready to enter, save, edit, retrieve, and perform other data manipulations.

· **Addresses**   Each cell is identified by a combination of a letter and a number to locate it in the spreadsheet. Letters for each column are shown across the top of the worksheet and begin to repeat with two letter combinations after Z is reached. This continues until the final column is reached, which is the 256th column, labeled IV. Rows continue numerically until the last row, 16,384, is reached.

P.5.1 Activating a Cell or Range of Cells

When the spreadsheet is initially opened, Cell A1 is automatically the active cell. It has a dark outline around it, which indicates that whatever you type will be entered into that cell. Note that the address A1 is displayed in the Name Box, which is to the left of the Formula Bar. Move to another cell, click, and note the change in the Name Box.

Often we need to refer to more than one cell at a time. A group of cells is called a **Range**. Click on cell B4, hold the mouse button down and drag down to B8. Release the button. The screen is now darkened (highlighted) in the range of cells, except for the top cell, B4. To indicate the address of a range of cells, we separate the addresses of the upper left and lower right cells with a colon. Here we have a range identified as B4:B8, although the Name Box only indicates the address of the top cell.

To activate cells in many rows and columns (i.e., a range) place the cursor in the upper left cell and drag to the lower right. Now all of the cells in that range will appear shaded. You can click and drag in the opposite direction if you wish. This is handier if you tend to overshoot your target and continue on past where you want to end, as many of us do. Another way to activate a range of cells is to click in the upper left cell, move to the lower right cell using the scroll bars or arrows, and then press the SHIFT key and click on the lower right cell (SHIFT + CLICK ON CELL) at the same time. Now all cells between these two points are shaded.

P.5.2 Types of Information

There are three types of information that you can enter into a cell:

1. Text. This is the term used by Excel developers. Other spreadsheet programs may call the alphabetic characters typed in a cell "labels."

2. Numbers. Most often you will enter numerical data.

3. Formulas. These cause new information generated from operations performed on text and numbers that are entered in cells.

P.5.3 Changing information

To change information in a cell, you have to consider which of two situations exist:

- If you have not yet "accepted" the information by clicking the green check mark (or pressing enter, or using arrow keys, or ...) then you can simply use the backspace or delete keys to remove entries. Insert the **I-beam** at the point where you want to change something and use the backspace key to remove characters to its left and the delete key to remove them at its right.

- If you are typing information into a cell and decide you want to start over, click on the red X and everything will be deleted.

- If you just want to delete everything in the **active cell** or range of cells, press the delete button.

- If you have already entered and accepted data in a cell, but now want to go back to edit it but not erase all of it, activate the cell and then insert the I-beam in the editing window where you want to make the changes.

As a practice exercise for changing information, try going through the following steps:

- In cell A1 type 12346. Press Enter, which moves you to A2.

- Assume you really wanted to enter 123456.

- Return to A1 by using the arrow key or mouse.

- Move the mouse pointer so the I-beam is between 4 and 6 in the editing bar. Click once.

- Note that the three editing keys are now shown to the left of 12346.

- Type 5, which will be inserted between 4 and 6.

A1	▼	X	√	fx	12346

	A	B	C
1	12346		
2			
3			
4			
5			
6			

P.5.4 Moving and copying information

A basic principle used in many programs is that you mark or indicate which material will have something done to it by first marking it and then execute the command that does something to the highlighted material. We will see this principle operate in several other places in the program. When we want to move information we can do it so that it is removed from one location and placed in another. This is a **cut**. If we want to make a copy of the material so that it in is the original location as well as in other locations we make a **copy**. Help for each of these procedures is obtained by searching the Help menu using the words *cutting* or *copying*.

To copy the entry in cell A1 (123456) to cell B1 we first mark the cell by clicking on it. Move the mouse pointer to the icon for copy or use **Edit - Copy**. The outline around the cell will become like the lights on a marquee; it will alternately darken and lighten. It is ready to be copied. Click the cell where you want the copy, say A2. Use the **Edit - Paste** commands or the icon for paste to place a copy there. Copy operates like a rubber stamp; we have a copy stored in the Clipboard and can continue to place copies anywhere we wish. Activate another cell, say C3 and paste another copy there.

Cutting is done in a similar fashion, except that the cell is empty after you cut the data from it. Click on any cell with content, say A1, and then click on the cut icon in the standard toolbar, which is a pair of scissors. The cell will be outlined, as it was when you used *copy*. Activate another cell and click on the icon for pasting, the same one used before.

If you cut or copy a group of cells, i.e., a range, the principle is the same. Instead of activating one cell, you click and drag over the cells so that a range of cells is now marked. Pasting is the same, except that the upper left cell of the group is the one whose location you specify as the target for the cut or copy.

Moving material between worksheets is accomplished the same way. You mark, indicate the cut or copy, move to the new sheet and the location on that sheet, and then paste.

  · **Dragging and dropping.**   If you want to cut or copy a range of cells on the same sheet, a shortcut to use is called **drag and drop**. Mark the cells, move the cursor to an edge, where it will become an outline arrow, hold down the mouse and drag to the new location. That is for cutting. To copy, hold down the **CTRL** key at the same time. If you attempt to drag and drop material onto a spot that currently has data in it you will get a message that asks if you want to do this, because it will remove the old material. If you have mistakenly done this, you can fall back on the **Undo Drag and Drop** command that you will find in the **Edit** menu. For more information, look up *drag and drop* in the help menu.

P. 6 Formatting numbers

Start with a clean spreadsheet. You can clear everything from a sheet by marking the whole sheet (Press CTRL+A) and then pressing the Delete key. Or, you can simply move to another sheet by clicking on a tab at the bottom of the screen. Enter these numbers into A1 through A6 and then copy them into column B, C, D and E.

| | Arial | | 10 | | **B** | *I* | U | ≡ | ≡ | ≡ | 📊 | $ | % | , | +.0 .00 | .00 +.0 |

| | E1 | ▼ | | 123456700% |

	A	B	C	D	E	F
1	1234567	#######	$1,234,567.00	$1,234,567	123456700%	
2	234567	#######	$ 234,567.00	$234,567	23456700%	
3	34567	#######	$ 34,567.00	$34,567	3456700%	
4	4567	#######	$ 4,567.00	$4,567	456700%	
5	567	$ 567.00	$ 567.00	$567	56700%	
6	67	$ 67.00	$ 67.00	$67	6700%	
7						
8						

- **Currency** Click on the B at the top of the second column to mark it. On the formatting bar you will find a $. Click on it. The initial column width is set at 8.43. With this width, column B looks like the one shown above; all but the last two figures are replaced by ###. When you see this, it indicates that the numbers are too long to fit in that width. We can readjust the column width by double-clicking between the B and C at the top of the column. To show how this will change the appearance, we will activate column C, click on the $ icon and then double-click on the vertical separation between C and D to widen it an appropriate amount. The figure shows what results.

- **Currency variations** If you wish to change to the format which has no decimal, click on **Format - Cells**. The dialog box that results indicates the options regarding the number of decimals and the presence or absence of the $. In column E we used this feature to eliminate the cents.

- **Percent and comma** These options are to the right of the **Currency** option. Try them and note the changes. A number like 567 becomes 56700%.

- **Changing the decimal** The two icons to the right of the icon for inserting a comma allow you to increase or decrease the number of places displayed to the right of the decimal. Try these on data you have marked.

P.6. 1 Aligning Information

Start with a clearly unaligned set of data, such as the following:

| | A8 | ▼ | | 0.1234567 |

	A	B	C	D
1	1234567			
2	123456.7			
3	12345.67			
4	1234.567			
5	123.4567			
6	12.34567			
7	1.234567			
8	0.123457			
9				

Notice what happens when you enter the last row. It displays 0.123457. The six is missing. The program has been set to display digits to six places to the right of the decimal, if there is space. It rounds off any values that exceed that size. Enter .00001234567. The rounded value of 0.001235 is displayed, but the unrounded number is shown in the edit window. Moving on to .00001234567 you will see the value displayed as 1.23E-05, the exponential form of the number. We will not be concerned with these in this book, but they are commonly used in scientific measurements.

A simple way to align the eight entries above is to mark them and then click on the comma icon. Commas will be placed appropriately and values shown to two decimals. The last entry is displayed as 0.12. As above, the Formula Bar will display what we entered, .1234567, and that is the figure that will be used in computations. You can increase or decrease the number of decimals displayed, as described previously.

P.6.2 Formatting a range

Format a range of cells by marking it and applying the formatting style as was just demonstrated. You can use the Format command on the Menu Bar, followed by the Styles Dialog Box to select the style desired and the number of decimals to display.

P.6.3 Inserting or deleting rows and columns

Inserting or deleting rows and columns is relatively easy. If you have entered data in a row that includes columns A, B, and C and want to place a new column between A and B, do this: Click on the letter B to mark that column. On the Main Menu Bar, select Insert, and then click on **Columns**. You can continue, inserting as many columns as you wish by continuing to click the mouse.

If you are starting over and want to insert two columns between A and B, simply mark columns B and C at the same time and follow the procedure above. To delete these two empty columns, mark them and go to the Edit command and click Delete.

The procedure for inserting or deleting rows is exactly the same, except that you use the numbers for the rows instead of the column letters.

P.6.4 Filling adjacent cells

Filling can mean one of two things. Filling can mean that you take the contents of a given cell or range of cells and make copies of that material in adjacent cells. Filling, broadly defined, can also mean that you continue a series or sequence of content into adjacent cells. For example, you might want to list the day of the week, and begin by typing Sunday into cell A1 and Monday into cell A2. You then can continue with Tuesday through Sunday in cells A3 through A8 with a simple move. We will discuss this in the section on **Series**.

Filling the same content into adjacent cells:

To learn how to fill the same content into adjacent cells, follow the steps below:

- On a clean spreadsheet, enter Sunday in cell A1 and Monday in cell A2.

- Click in the center of cell A1 and drag to cell A7, activating that range.

- At the menu bar, choose *Edit - Fill* and click on *Down*.

- Now you will have Sunday copied in all the cells from A1 through A7

Copying takes the contents of the first cell in a series of marked cells and duplicates throughout the marked cells. The content of the second cell, Monday, is removed.

Filling a Series into Adjacent Cells

To learn how to fill a series into adjacent cells, follow the steps presented below:

- As above, enter Sunday in cell A1 and Monday in cell A2.

- Make sure Monday is entered by tapping Enter or clicking on the green check mark.

- Click in the center of cell A1 and drag through A2 so both cells are marked.

- Place the mouse pointer on the black dot (the **fill handle**) at the lower right of the two cells.

- The mouse pointer changes to a solid black plus sign. Drag it to cell A7.

The **series** of days from Sunday through Saturday is listed.

An easier method of accomplishing the same thing is presented below:

- Use the above layout of Sunday in cell A1 and Monday in cell A2

- Click on A1 to activate it.

- Grab the fill handle of cell A1 and drag to A7 to complete the series.

Days of the week are special, since we have a given order determined by convention. If we choose numbers that have no agreed upon sequence, we will not get a series generated by simply choosing the first number on the list.

We can also generate a series of numbers, but the series must have an identifiable pattern.

- On a clean spreadsheet, enter 10 in A1 and 15 in A2.

- Mark A1 and A2 by dragging over them.

- Using the fill handle, drag to A10

- You should have the numbers 10, 15, 20, 25, ... to 55 listed.

P.6.5 Series

The above activities show how easily we can copy the contents of a given cell into adjacent cells or generate a series of numbers from two examples. Now we will use the **series** command to generate a series of numbers.

Follow the steps presented below.

- Enter these numbers in cells A1:A3: 5, 7, 9.

- Activate the range A1:A10.

- Using *Edit - Fill - Series* will produce the dialog box shown below that provides information about the series for you to verify before the program continues the series.

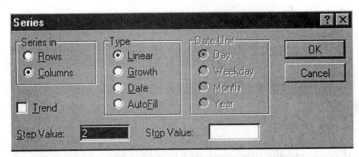

The dialog box displays the program's interpretation of the data. The series is presented in **Columns**. It is a **Linear** relationship. No **Date Units** are provided. The **Step Value** and **Stop Value** are available for verification and determination. If you wanted to specify a value to stop at, it would be entered in that box.

P.6.6 Sorting

Sorting becomes a useful tool when we have a set of data to analyze and want an initial look to see how it is distributed. First mark the data to be sorted and then use the **Data - Sort** commands. There are other ways to sort that we will also describe. Enter the data as shown below into a fresh spreadsheet.

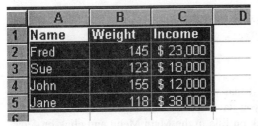

A dialog box, shown below, requires that we specify which column to use in sorting:

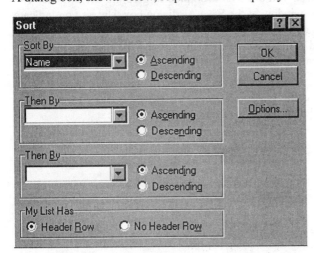

The upper left cell, activated when we marked the range, is listed as the default variable to use. We also have the choice of sorting ascending or descending order, using that column. At the bottom of the box we have to indicate if the row at the top is data or titles of the variables. It is correctly marked. If we click OK, the following sort results:

	A	B	C
1	Name	Weight	Income
2	Fred	145	$ 23,000
3	Jane	118	$ 38,000
4	John	155	$ 12,000
5	Sue	123	$ 18,000

Names are now arranged in alphabetical order and the data connected to each name has been moved along with it. Try the above sort, but instead of accepting *Name* as the variable to use in sorting, click on the down arrow, which shows Weight and Income as other choices to use.

Note that we have three options for sorting. In this case we have no data that is the same for a variable, e.g. no two people weigh the same. If, for example we had a list of 100 student members of an organization that included active and former membership status and address (street, city, zip code), then we would have a number of zip codes that are identical. In this case we might want to sort by zip code, and then by membership status if we were generating mailing labels (sorted by zip code for a cheaper rate) and different messages for different types of members. The one identifier that should not have any duplicates is social security account number, which is why it is often used as an identifier.

P.7 Saving and retrieving information

P.7.1 Naming workbooks

Earlier versions of Excel used one sheet as the basic unit that was stored as one file. Now, up to 256 sheets can be stored as one unit, called a workbook. If you have opened a new workbook and entered data that you want to save, the logical next step is to click on File in the Main Menu and click on *Save*. When you have a new, previously unnamed sheet, you are then prompted to give the file a name. The default name of Book1 appears in the File Name window of the Save As dialog box. Unless you indicate otherwise, the file will be saved in the last location used, be it the hard drive, network server, or diskette. A common default is to save in a folder called *My Documents*, which is found by clicking on the file folder icon having an asterisk (*) in it. This is called *Favorites*. The following figure shows the *Save As* dialog box:

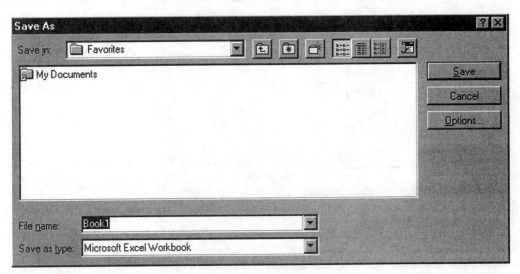

In version 7.0 of Excel, using Windows 95, files can have names longer than eight letters. In earlier versions, the **DOS** naming convention applies. In that case, a file cannot nave a name longer than eight letters, followed by a period and an extension, usually .xls. A typical file name might be Bus101hw.xls. There are restrictions on the symbols that you can use in a file name, which will be apparent when you get an error message for using a / or some other forbidden symbols. Windows 95, and earlier Mac versions allow names to have up to 256 characters, so they can be more descriptive of the contents. Use the *?* and *Hel*p to learn the names and functions of the various boxes in the *Save As* dialog box.

P.8 Printing

P.8.1 Page Setup

The **Page Setup** dialog box displays four tabs along the top to access the four options: **Page**, **Margins**, **Header/Footer**, and **Sheet**. It is accessed by going to File - Page Setup.

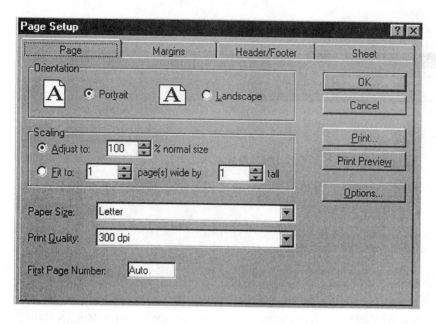

P.8.2 Page

Page allows the user to change the **orientation** of the page from portrait (the way this book is printed) to landscape (sideways). With the **scaling** commands you can adjust the size of the image to be 10% of normal size or enlarge it to 400%. The **Fit to** command instructs the program to automatically adjust the size to fit any of a number of pages as specified.

> Beware: If you have three or four pages of material to print and direct the program to fit it to one page, it is sometimes difficult to read. You can specify that it will stay one page high and allow it to continue to the right on other sheets as far as necessary by using the two adjustments available.

Paper Size and **Print Quality** provide options shown via the drop-down arrow, although most often letter size paper is used, and print quality adjustments are not available. On some printers, you can move to a higher quality print by changing the dpi to a value of 600 or more. This does increase printing time and use of ink.

Clicking on **Options** provides more graphic views of some of these choices, depending on your printer.

First Page Number is set to **Auto** as the default. If you wish to start the page numbering at a specific value, type in that value after highlighting **Auto**.

P.8.3 Margins

Margins are set using the options shown by clicking the Margins tab. The preview window shows how these will look as you change them. Note that you can also center the output on the page horizontally, vertically, or both. After you have changed any of the settings you can click on **Print Preview...** to check its appearance. You can also change the margins in Print Preview by dragging the margin boundary handles.

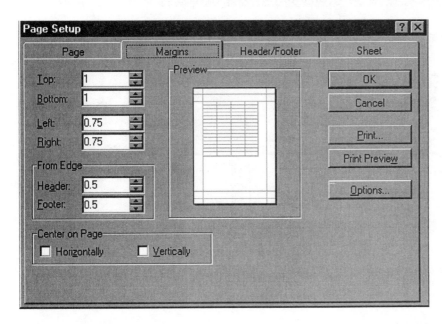

P.8.4 Header/Footer

Headers contain the information printed across the top of all (or all but the first) pages. In this text the headers on one page indicate the chapter title and page number; on the other we have the section and page number. Sometimes this information is printed at the bottom of a page, and called a **Footer**. Our descriptions of the procedures for developing headers also applies to footers.

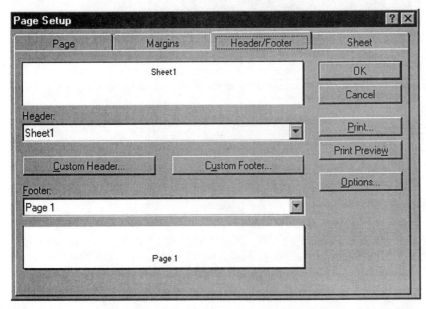

Unless you alter the settings, the **header** and **footer** shown above are the default. Click on the arrow to the right of the default header and you will see some previously used on the computer. You may wish to choose one of them and edit it to your liking. Or, if you wish, you can click on **Options...** and obtain the following dialog box:

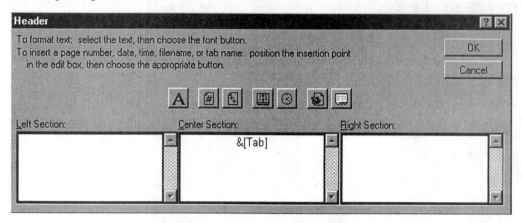

In this case, you have the option to place your header in the left, center, or right of the page. Use the ? and the help to determine what the icons will do for you. The letter A, when clicked, allows you to write in text, changing the font and size; others are for page numbering, date and time, filename and sheetname.

P.8.5 Sheet

This page allows you to choose the area to print, whether to print titles of columns or rows on sheets that continue on to other sheets, print gridlines, the quality of print, and row and column headings. Click on the ? and point to each of the areas to learn how to use them.

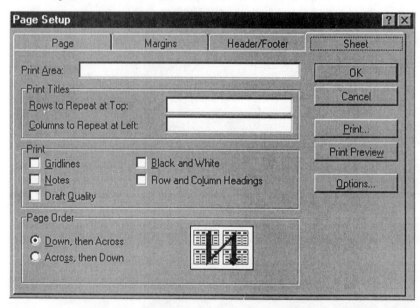

Print Area allows you to select a given range to print. Simply click in the box to the right and then move to the spreadsheet where you drag to indicate the range to select. On Version 7 you will have to grab the above window by the title bar to move it away from the area you want to mark. Version 8 has an option for briefly collapsing this dialog box to more easily do this.

P.8.6 Enhancing output

With a bit of experience you can improve the appearance of your output by using the options described above. Using the preview option allows you to see exactly how things will look before you print them. Sometimes gridlines improve the display. An enlarged title adds clarity. Size of the sheet can be adjusted for your purposes. All of these can be explored using the options above.

P.8.7 Inserting and removing page breaks

When a worksheet spans more than one page, Excel determines where to insert a page break. You might find it more convenient to make the break at a different location. Use the Help function to look up *page breaks* in the index for directions. If you have used *Page* in Page Setup to fit everything onto one page, it may not appear as you wish, especially if the material takes up less than one page. Page Preview is always a good way to determine what looks best.

P.8.8 Preview and print

Clever computer users preview their material before they print it. You can go to the Print Preview command under File or simply click the icon on the Standard Toolbar. To change options, after you view your sample, you can use the menu at the top. Try out such things as Zoom, which will increase the size of the page so you can view details. Click it to turn it on and click it to return to the full page view. Setup will display the four pages described above, in that section. Margins will display lines on your preview that shows where the margins will be located. You can grab the handles and change them on the sheet. Close returns you to the regular view of the page. Print moves you to the dialog box with choices regarding the printer to use, number of copies, which pages to print, etc.

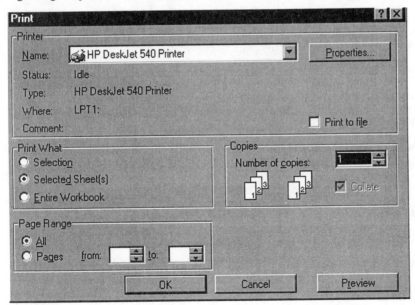

P.9 Using Formulas and Functions

P.9.1 Operators

Algebraic formulas utilize the four common operations of addition (+), subtraction (-), multiplication (x), and division (÷).When creating formulas, we will use these operations along with three others. Called **operators**, they are symbolized as:

Addition +   Multiplication *   Subtraction –   Division /

Negation refers to using the minus sign to indicate a negative number, as in –3

Exponentiation ^   Percent %

Multiplication uses an asterisk instead of an x. Division uses a diagonal (/) instead of the division symbol. If we wish to raise a value to a power, say X^2 we place the carat (^) between the X and the 2. To raise a number X to the second power, we would write X^2. Finally, we can also place a percent (%) sign behind a value, as in 20%. For example, the formula 15 ^ 2 * 15% raises 15 to the second power and multiplies the result by 0.15 (the decimal form of 15%) to produce the result of 33.75.

We also group sets of operations together with parentheses, which determines the order of execution of commands by the computer. Any operations enclosed in parentheses are executed first, moving from the innermost parentheses to the outermost.

P.9.2 Order of Operations

The order of operations in Excel is:

1. Negation, as in –15

2. Percent

3. Exponentiation

4. Multiplication and division

5. Addition and subtraction

Excel first calculates expressions in parentheses and then uses those results to complete the calculation of the formula. For example

= 2+4*3   produces 14 because multiplication occurs before addition

= (2+4)*3   produces 18 because operations within parentheses are executed first

= 2+(4*3)   produces 14 because operations within parentheses are executed first

In a more complex situation,

= 2+(4*(3+5)^2)/2   produces 130.

First the terms in the innermost parentheses are executed, producing 8. Then this is raised to the second power, producing 64, since this is within the second set of parentheses and exponentiation has precedence over the other operations. 64 is multiplied by 4, yielding 256. This is divided by 2, producing

128. Finally added to 2 yields 130. Try this on your computer, by entering this formula into cell A1 and pressing Enter.

P.9.3 Writing Equations

In the equations above, we have always used numeric constants, such as 2, 3, 4, or 5. In practice, the formula that you write will probably refer to a cell that may contain any value. This is equivalent to the X and Y that acted as unknowns in algebra. For example, to convert degrees Fahrenheit to Celsius, we use the formula:

C = 5/9(F-32).

Let's set up a table to provide this conversion. Type the label in cell A1: *Degrees Fahrenheit*. In cell B1 type: *Degrees Celsius*. Enter the two values of –60 and –59 in cells A2 and A3. That's a good place to start if you live in Wisconsin in January.

	A	B
1	Degrees Fahrenheit	Degrees Celsius
2		
3	-60	
4	-59	
5		
6		
7		

Let Excel continue the series by clicking on the value of –60 and dragging down to cell A80 to mark those cells. Then go to Edit – Fill – Series and notice that the program has correctly inferred that the step size is +1. Each time we move down a row the value in column A is reduced by one unit. We wish to continue the series with that change. Click OK and we have data extending from –60 to17 degrees. In cell B3 enter this formula:

=5/9(A3-32)   and press Enter.

When the temperature is -60 degrees Fahrenheit, it is -51.11 degrees Celsius, as cell B3 indicates. Activate cell B3. Now, just click on the small square in the lower right of cell B3 (the fill handle), and drag to cell B80. The screen pointer becomes a solid black plus sign when you use the fill handle. You have copied the formula into all of those cells, with the address of each cell that represents degrees Fahrenheit changing for each row. You should have something like the following:

	A	B
1	Degrees Fahrenheit	Degrees Celsius
2		
3	-60	-51.11111111
4	-59	-50.55555556
5	-58	-50
6	-57	-49.44444444
7	-56	-48.88888889
8	-55	-48.33333333
9	-54	-47.77777778
10	-53	-47.22222222
11	-52	-46.66666667
12	-51	-46.11111111
13	-50	-45.55555556
14	-49	-45

To make our output more attractive, click on column B to activate that column, go to Format – Cells – Number and accept the default of two places to the right of the decimal. Now you should have the first few rows of data looking like this:

	A	B
1	Degrees Fahrenheit	Degrees Celsius
2		
3	-60	-51.11
4	-59	-50.56
5	-58	-50.00
6	-57	-49.44
7	-56	-48.89
8	-55	-48.33
9	-54	-47.78
10	-53	-47.22
11	-52	-46.67
12	-51	-46.11
13	-50	-45.56
14	-49	-45.00

P.10 Entering Formulas

Now let's take a situation that is very commonly used by students. Compute a Grade Point Average. Enter the following information in a new blank spreadsheet:

	A	B	C	D
1	Course	Credits:	Grade:	Value:
2				
3	English	5	A	4
4	Math	4	B	3
5	Psychology	3	A	4
6	Economics	3	C	2
7		15		
8				
9	Grade:	Value:		
10	F	0		
11	D	1		
12	C	2		
13	B	3		
14	A	4		

We want to compute the Grade Point Average. We have to multiply the credits for a course by the value of the grade given for that course. In Cell E3 enter this formula: =B3*D3. Then use the fill handle in the cell to copy the formula from E3 to E6, so that you have the product of credits times value of grade for each course. The recommended procedure for setting up formulas is to click on the cell whose address you want entered, NOT type in the address of that cell. In this case you would type the = sign in E3 and then click on B3, which now appears in the formula. Then enter an asterisk (from either SHIFT-8 or the * key on the keypad) followed by clicking on D3. Then either click on Enter or the green arrow in the formula bar. You should have:

	A	B	C	D	E
1	Course:	Credits:	Grade:	Value:	Grade Points:
2					
3	English	5	A	4	20
4	Math	4	B	3	12
5	Psychology	3	A	4	12
6	Economics	3	C	2	6
7					
8					
9	Grade:	Value:			
10	F	0			
11	D	1			
12	C	2			
13	B	3			
14	A	4			

Now all we need to do is to sum the Grade Points, sum the Credits, and then divide Grade Points by Credits to get GPA. Use the AutoSum button, Σ (a Greek Sigma on the Standard Toolbar) to obtain the sum for each. Just activate cell B7 and click on that button. A series of dotted lines surrounds the four digits above, indicating that the program estimates that this is what you want to sum. Click Enter and the value of 15 will be displayed. Do the same for the Grade Points to obtain 50. To obtain the GPA you can enter those two values in an equation directly or enter the cell references in the equation to obtain the answer. If you do the latter, your equation would look like: = E7/B7. Put your answer in cell E10 as shown below:

	A	B	C	D	E
1	Course	Credits:	Grade:	Value:	Grade Points:
2					
3	English	5	A	4	20
4	Math	4	B	3	12
5	Psychology	3	A	4	12
6	Economics	3	C	2	6
7		15			50
8					
9	Grade:	Value:		GPA=	3.333333333
10	F	0			
11	D	1			
12	C	2			
13	B	3			
14	A	4			

Note that the value of 3.3333... doesn't appear until you press Enter or click on the green arrow. If you click on cell E9 now, the formula you used to obtain that value will be displayed in the Formula Bar, not the value shown here. For emphasis, you can mark cells D9 and E9 and then click on the symbol to make them **BOLD**.

P.10.1 Relative References

When we entered the formula for determining Grade Points in cell E3, we entered it using the relative reference mode. We told the program to go to cell B3, obtain that value, go to cell D3, obtain that value, multiply them and place the answer in E3. Actually we instructed Excel to move three cell locations to the left (B3) of the active cell, obtain that number, move one cell to the left (D3) of the active cell, obtain that number, multiply them and place the answer in the active cell. To see how this works, try this: Activate cell E3. Note the formula in the Formula Bar. Now activate cell F3. The formula references in the formula bar have been adjusted to reflect what was said above; the program is not going to absolute locations of cells, but is moving relative to the active cell, using the same movements in the spreadsheet that were specified in the formula. Now let's make our computation of the GPA a bit more sophisticated by using that table that gives the value of each grade. We will use a function called **table lookup**.

P.10.2 Absolute References

When we have a table that converts a letter grade to a corresponding number (or vice versa), we can use a built-in function known as **VLOOKUP**. Mark cells D3 through D6 and press delete to clear the contents. We will have the program **VLOOKUP** compare the grade letter printed in cells C3 through C6 to the tabled values in cells A10:B14 to fill in the number value corresponding to a letter grade. Click on the Function Wizard (the f_x on the Standard **Toolbar**). Move to the **Lookup & Reference** part of the Paste Function Window as shown below. Click on **VLOOKUP** as indicated. Then click OK.

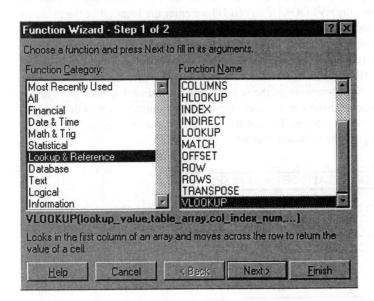

Function Wizard - Step 1 of 2

Choose a function and press Next to fill in its arguments.

Function Category:

Most Recently Used
All
Financial
Date & Time
Math & Trig
Statistical
Lookup & Reference
Database
Text
Logical
Information

Function Name

COLUMNS
HLOOKUP
INDEX
INDIRECT
LOOKUP
MATCH
OFFSET
ROW
ROWS
TRANSPOSE
VLOOKUP

VLOOKUP(lookup_value,table_array,col_index_num,...)

Looks in the first column of an array and moves across the row to return the value of a cell.

Help   Cancel   < Back   Next >   Finish

The following window appears after you execute the above and enter the values into the formula as shown in the formula bar. After we enter the =VLOOKUP in cell D3 we enter the location of the grade to translate (cell C3), then the absolute address of the table ($A$10:$B$14), the letter 2 to indicate that we want the number from the second column in the table, followed by FALSE which indicates that we want an exact match. After accepting the formula by clicking the green arrow, we use the fill handle to copy the formula into cells D4: D6. The cells $A$10:$B$14 are absolute references because we do not want them to change as we refer to them in the operations on the second, third, and fourth grades. Whenever we want an address to be absolute, we preface the usual column letter and row number with a dollar sign. The figure below shows the formula entered into cell D3 and the resulting value of 4. Note how the C3 value is a relative value while references to the table are absolute.

D3			=VLOOKUP(C3,$A$10:$B$14,2,FALSE)		
	A	B	C	D	E	F
1	Course	Credits:	Grade:	Value:	Grade Points:	
2						
3	English	5	A	4	20	
4	Math	4	B	3	12	
5	Psychology	3	A	4	12	
6	Economics	3	C	2	6	
7		15			50	
8						
9	Grade:	Value:		GPA=	3.333333333	
10	F	0				
11	D	1				
12	C	2				
13	B	3				
14	A	4				
15						

Chapter 1
Statistics, Data, and Statistical Thinking

1.1 Introduction

Chapter 1 introduces the topics that will be expanded on throughout the text. No data analysis is necessary in Chapter 1 and Microsoft Excel® cannot be used here in the text.

Chapter 1
Statistics, Data, and Statistical Thinking

1.1 Introduction

Chapter 2
Methods For Describing Sets of Data

2.1 Introduction

Chapter 1 served to introduce many of the basic statistical concepts employed in all types of data analysis problems. Two main areas of statistics emerge from Chapter 1 - descriptive and inferential statistics. Chapter 2 focuses on the descriptive area and looks at both graphical and numerical techniques that allow statisticians to summarize data that has been collected. Many of the techniques used to summarize data discussed in *Statistics for Business and Economics* can easily be performed with Excel. Our purpose is to explain these techniques and to illustrate them using the examples presented in the text as well as additional examples provided here. Listed below are the various techniques that Excel offers that can be used to generate the graphical and numerical topics presented in Chapter 2.

Excel offers a wide array of graphing options to the statistician. When working with qualitative data, Excel allows the statistician to create customized **pie charts** and **bar graphs**. For quantitative data, **histograms** and **scatter plots** are easy to create. The scatter plot feature in Excel can readily be used to create the **time series plot** discussed in the text. At the present time, Excel does not allow the creation of **dot plots** or **stem-and-leaf-displays**.

As with most database and statistical software programs, Excel provides a wide array of numerical descriptions of data. The three measures of central tendency (**mean, median,** and **mode**) and the three measures of variability (**range, variance,** and **standard deviation**) are all available in the descriptive statistics menu of Excel. Measures of relative standing (**percentiles, quartiles,** and **z-scores***)* are available in Excel but not as easy to access as the measures of central tendency and measures of spread. The **box plots** discussed in Chapter 2 are not available in Excel.

The following examples from *Statistics for Business and Economics* are solved with Microsoft Excel® in this chapter:

Excel Companion		Statistics for Business and Economics	
Example	**Page**	**SBE Example**	**SBE Page**
2.1	36	2.2	40
2.2	42	2.1	29
2.3	45	2.18	91
2.4	49	2.5	54
2.5	51	2.10	66
2.6	53	2.10	66
2.7	55	2.10	66

2.2 Graphical Techniques in Excel

2.2.1 Bar Graphs and Histograms

Bar graphs, pie charts, and scatter plots are all easy to generate using Excel. The graphs enable the user to summarize the data that they are viewing and make decisions quickly and easily. We first look at creating bar graphs (or histograms) within Excel.

Example 2.1: As an example, we turn to Example 2.2 from *Statistics for Business and Economics* found on pages 40-42 of the text:

A manufacturer of industrial wheels suspects that profitable orders are being lost because of the long time the firm takes to develop price quotes for potential customers. To investigate this possibility, 50 requests for price quotes were randomly selected from the set of all quotes made last year, and the processing time was determined for each quote. The processing times are displayed below in Table 2.1, and each quote was classified according to whether the order was "lost" or not (i.e., whether or not the customer placed an order after receiving a price quote).

Table 2.1

Request	Time	Lost?	Request	Time	Lost?
1	2.36	No	26	3.34	No
2	5.73	No	27	6.00	No
3	6.60	No	28	5.92	No
4	10.05	Yes	29	7.28	Yes
5	5.13	No	30	1.25	No
6	1.88	No	31	4.01	No
7	2.52	No	32	7.59	No
8	2.00	No	33	13.42	Yes
9	4.69	No	34	3.24	No
10	1.91	No	35	3.37	No
11	6.75	Yes	36	14.06	Yes
12	3.92	No	37	5.10	No
13	3.46	No	38	6.44	No
14	2.64	No	39	7.76	No
15	3.63	No	40	4.40	No
16	3.44	No	41	5.48	No
17	9.49	Yes	42	7.51	No
18	4.90	No	43	6.18	No
19	7.45	No	44	8.22	Yes
20	20.23	Yes	45	4.37	No
21	3.91	No	46	2.93	No
22	1.70	No	47	9.95	Yes
23	16.29	Yes	48	4.46	No
24	5.52	No	49	14.32	Yes
25	1.44	No	50	9.01	No

a.   Use a statistical software package to create a frequency histogram for these data. Then shade the area under the histogram that corresponds to lost orders.

b.   Use a statistical software package to create a stem-and-leaf display for these data. Then shade each leaf that corresponds to a lost order.

c.   Compare and interpret the two graphical displays of these data.

We can use Excel to generate the histogram in part a. To do so we first must get access to the data set for the problem. If you are working with Excel97, you may simply **Open** the Excel file CX02_002. If you are working with other versions of Excel, you must **Import** the ASCII file CXA02_02.prn. Once the data is available for analysis, select the **Tools** icon from the top of the Excel worksheet. Choose the **Data Analysis** option from within the Tools menu. From the Data menu choose the **Histogram** option (see Figure 2.1). Click **OK**.

Figure 2.1

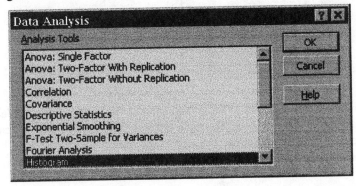

Perform these steps to enter the histogram menu within Excel. There are many options available within this menu. Our purpose here is to demonstrate the easiest method necessary to generate a histogram of the data, and to show the commands necessary to generate a histogram that matches the one shown in the text.

The easiest method to generate a histogram is shown in Figure 2.2. First, enter the rows and columns where the data is located in the **Input Range** of the histogram menu. This can be done by **typing** the location or by **clicking and dragging** over the appropriate data cells in your worksheet. The next step is to specify the **Output Range**. We have chose to begin the output at column F, row 1 by **typing F1** in the Output Range line of the histogram menu. We have the option in Excel97 to place this output in a new worksheet by specifying the New Worksheet Ply option. Finally, in order to generate the histogram, it is necessary to **check** the **Chart Output** option in the histogram menu. Click **OK**.

Figure 2.2

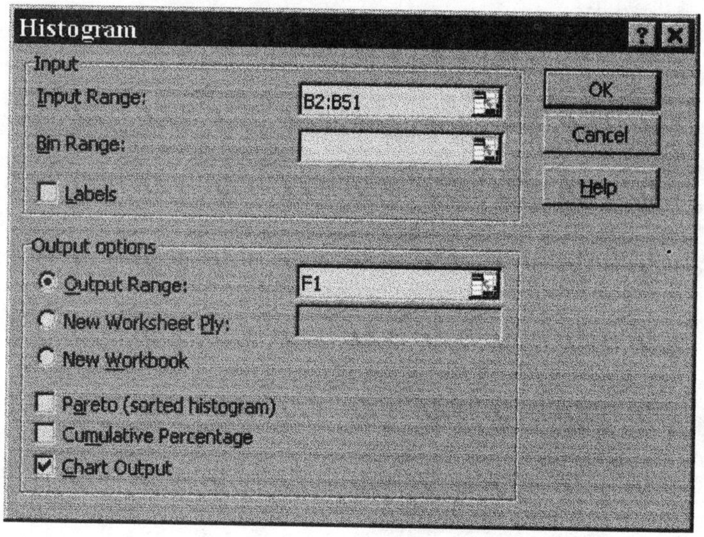

Excel generates two pieces of information and places this output beginning at the location we specified above. The first is a table of the data that is being charted. The table contains two pieces of information, Bin and Frequency. Bin (see Table 2.2) refers to the upper endpoint of the histogram bar that is to be drawn and Frequency is the number of observations that will be included in the corresponding bar.

Table 2.2

Bin	Frequency
1.25	1
3.961428571	17
6.672857143	16
9.384285714	8
12.09571429	3
14.80714286	3
17.51857143	1
More	1

Together, this information is used by Excel to generate the histogram (see Figure 2.3). The size of the histogram can be altered to make viewing the chart easier. Simply click on the histogram and stretch the squares on the outline of the histogram to make the display larger or smaller.

Figure 2.3

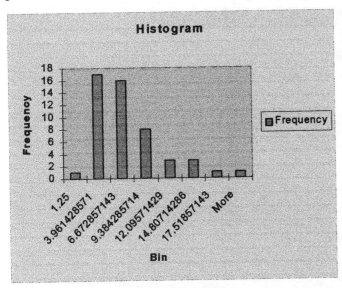

These commands generate a histogram that summarizes the data. Comparing this histogram to the one shown in the text, we see two major differences. First, this histogram has displayed the bars as being separated from one another, while the histogram in the text has bars that touch. The second difference is that the intervals, or interval endpoints, used in the two histograms differ. Both of these differences can be addressed using various options within Excel.

It is important to emphasize that no one histogram that is produced from the data is considered the "correct" one. Our purpose in duplicating the histogram presented in the text is to introduce the user to some of the many options that are available within the histogram menus of Excel. Producing a histogram comparable to the one in the book will allow for easier comparison with the stem-and-leaf display and for easier interpretation of the results.

The touching bars can be adjusted by **clicking** on any one of the bars generated in the histogram above. Next, select the **Format** option listed at the top of the Excel worksheet. Click on the **Selected Data Series** option. Select the **Options** tab of the Format Data Series menu (see Figure 2.4). The option that will allow the bars to touch is the **Gap Width** selection. Change the Gap Width to **0** to assign no gap between bars.

Figure 2.4

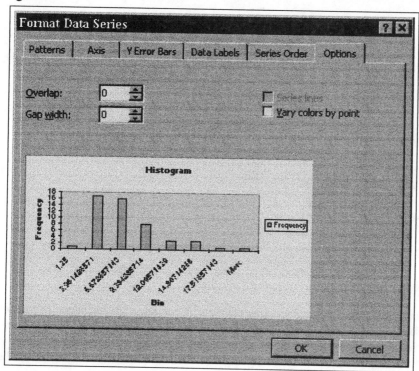

To change the intervals used by Excel requires the addition of a new column in the dataset used for the analysis. You must specify what Bin values that Excel should use to construct the histogram. The Bin values represent the largest endpoint of the bars generated in the chart. To duplicate the histogram presented in the text, with intervals of 2 days, the bar endpoints should be chosen at 3, 5, 7, 9, 11, 13, 15, 17, 18, and 21. This column of values must be entered alongside the data and chosen as the Bin Range (see Figures 2.5 and 2.6).

Figure 2.5

Bin Values
3
5
7
9
11
13
15
17
18
21

Figure 2.6

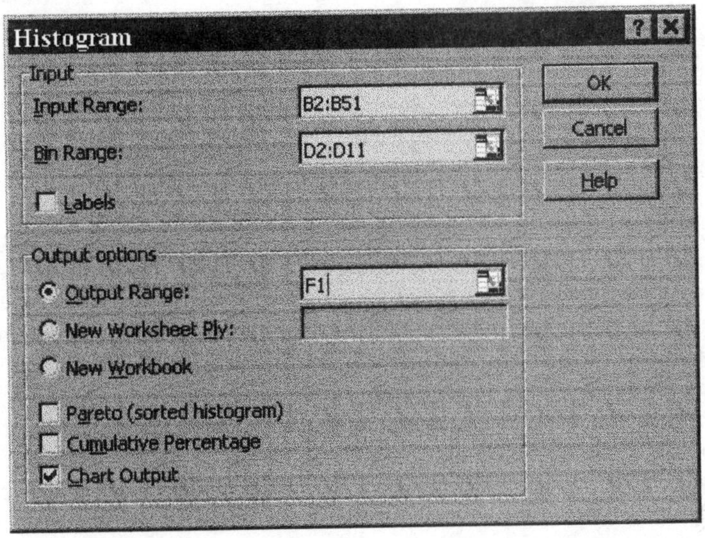

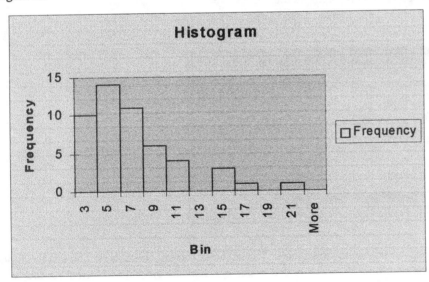

Together, these two changes can be used to produce a histogram that is like the one shown in the text (see Figure 2.7). Be sure to read through Example 2.2 in the text to understand how to interpret these results.

Figure 2.7

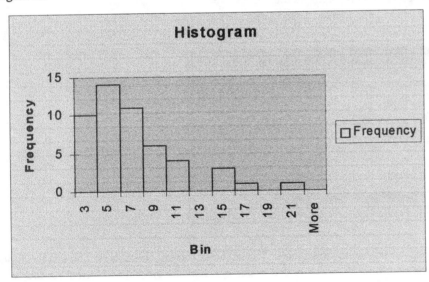

2.2.2 Pie Charts

The second type of graphical technique constructed by Excel is the pie chart. Since none of the chapter examples from *Statistics for Business and Economics* specifically ask for a pie chart, we will use the data from Example 2.1 and create the corresponding pie charts.

Example 2.2: *Statistics for Business and Economics* Example 2.1 found on pages 29-30

A group of cardiac physicians in southwest Florida have been studying a new drug designed to reduce blood loss in coronary artery bypass operations. Blood loss data for 114 coronary artery bypass patients (some of who received a dosage of the drug and others who did not) were collected and are made available for analysis. Although the drug shows promise in reducing blood loss, the physicians are concerned about possible side effects and complications. So their data set includes not only the qualitative variable, DRUG, which indicates whether or not the patient received the drug, but also the qualitative variable, COMP, which specifies the type (if any) of complication experienced by the patient. The four values of COMP recorded by the physician are: (1) redo surgery, (2) post-op infection, (3) both, or (4) none. Use the provided Excel data set to create a pie chart for the number and type of complications suffered by the two groups of patients (received drug/did not receive drug).

The first step in Excel is to **Open** the Excel data set CX02_001 (or the corresponding ASCII data set CXA02_01.prn) so that it can be analyzed. Constructing a pie chart follows the same basic steps that created the histograms from the preceding example. Choose the **Tools** icon from the top of the Excel worksheet. Choose the **Data Analysis** option from within the Tool menu. From the Data Analysis menu choose the **Histogram** option (see Figure 2.1 below). Click **OK**.

Figure 2.1

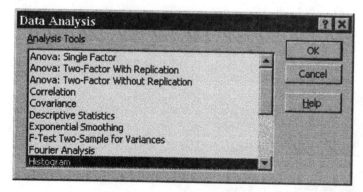

Follow the same path taken to create the histogram. This includes entering the data set range in the **Input Range** cell of the histogram menu. Note that in this example, a separate pie chart is desired for the "yes" and "no" groups of drug recipients. Note that only half the data will be used in each of the two pie charts generated. For purposes of this example, only the first half, the "no" drug recipients, will be used. Specify the desired location of the output in the **Output Range** cell of the menu. Again, make sure that the **Chart Output** box has been **checked** (see Figure 2.8). Click **OK**.

Once the histogram has been constructed, **click on the chart created** and you are now ready to change the type of chart created. Click on the **Chart** menu listed at the top of the Excel worksheet. Click on the

Chart Type option within the Chart menu. Choose the **Standard Types** tab in the Chart Types Menu.
Choose the **Pie** option from the list given in the Standard Tabs list (see Figure 2.9). Click **OK**. The
resulting pie chart is shown below in Figure 2.10.

Figure 2.8

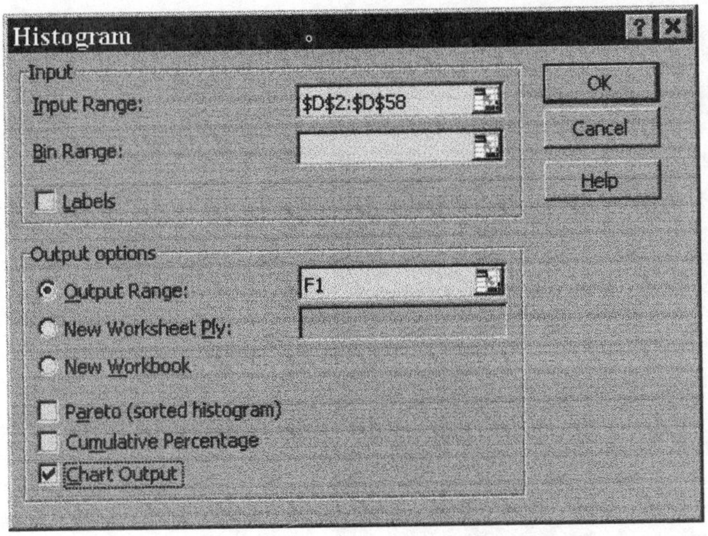

Figure 2.9

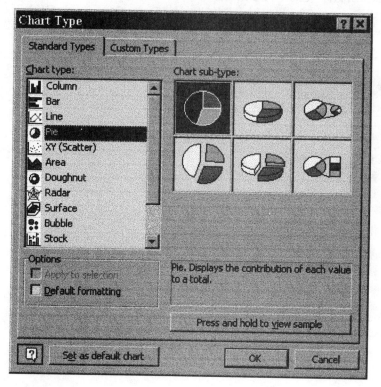

Figure 2.10

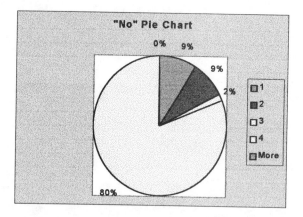

Two items should be kept in mind with this pie chart. First, another pie chart must be generated for the "yes" drug recipients as requested in the problem. The user must define the Input Range to be the complications developed by the "yes" recipients and follow the same procedure to generate the second pie chart. Second, Excel again allows the user many options to change the appearance of the pie chart. While too numerous to mention, the user may explore these options to get comfortable with the many choices Excel allows. Remember, the final appearance that you select should be pleasing to look at but never obscure the summarization that the pie chart was intended to make.

2.2.3 Scatter Plots

The final graphing technique discussed in *Statistics for Business and Economics* that can be constructed within Excel is the scatter plot. We use Example 2.18 from the text to demonstrate how to conduct a scatter plot.

Example 2.3: *Statistics for Business and Economics* Example 2.18 found on pages 91-93.

A medical item used to administer to a hospital patient is called a **factor**. For example, factors can be intravenous (IV) tubing, IV fluid, needles, shave kits, bedpans, diapers, dressings, medications, and even code carts. The coronary care unit at Bayonet Point Hospital (St. Petersburg, Florida) recently investigated the relationship between the number of factors administered per patient and the patient's length of stay (in days). Data on these two variables for a sample of 50 coronary care patients are given in Table 2.6. Use a scattergram to describe the relationship between the two variables of interest, number of factors and length of stay.

Table 2.6

Number of Factors	Length of Stay (in Days)	Number of Factors	Length of Stay (in Days)	Number of Factors	Length of Stay (in Days)
231	9	233	8	115	4
323	7	260	4	202	6
113	8	224	7	206	5
208	5	472	12	360	6
162	4	220	8	84	3
117	4	383	6	331	9
159	6	301	9	302	7
169	9	262	7	60	2
55	6	354	11	110	2
77	3	142	7	131	5
103	4	286	9	364	4
147	6	341	10	180	7
230	6	201	5	134	6
78	3	158	11	401	15
525	9	243	6	155	4
121	7	156	6	338	8
248	5	184	7		

Solution:

Excel offers a **Chart Wizard** to help create a variety of charts. It is easy to use and we now will demonstrate with the data from the example above. **Open** Excel file CX02_018 (or ASCII file CXA02_018.prn). To enter the Chart Wizard, Click on the **Insert** menu located at the top of the Excel worksheet. Click the **Chart** option within the Insert menu. **Highlight** the XY(Scatter) option within the Step 1 - Chart Type of the Chart Wizard (see Figure 2.11). **Click Next** to advance to Step 2 - Chart Source Data. Both variables to be plotted need to be included in the Data range entry within this menu. Make sure that the first row or column of data pertains to the variable to be plotted on the x-axis. The second row column of data should pertain to the y-axis variable. Enter this **Data Range** (see Figure 2.12) and **click Next**. Step 3 - Chart Options allows the user to specify many graphing options. We only mention that it is here that titles can be added to the scatter plot to ease the understanding of the graph (see Figure 2.13). We leave the user to experiment with the other options available at this step. **Clicking Next** allows the user to finish the Chart Wizard in Step 4 - Chart Location. The user may specify where the constructed scatter plot will appear in Excel (see Figure 2.14). Fill in the location as either a new worksheet or as an object and **click Finish**. The finished plot for this example appears in Figure 2.15.

Figure 2.11

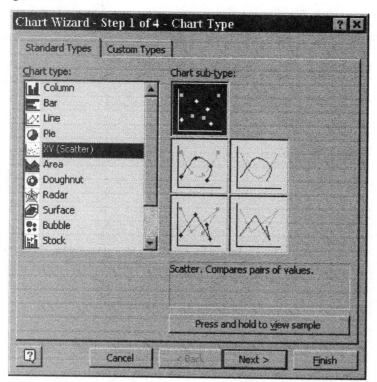

Figure 2.12

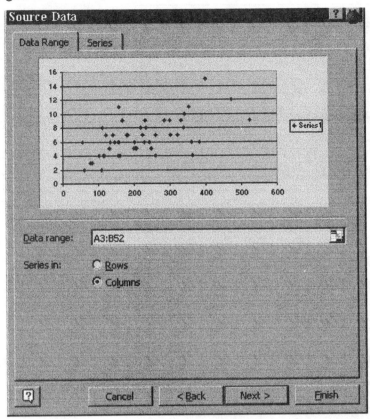

Figure 2.13

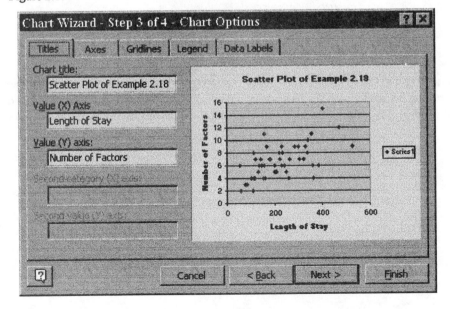

Figure 2.14

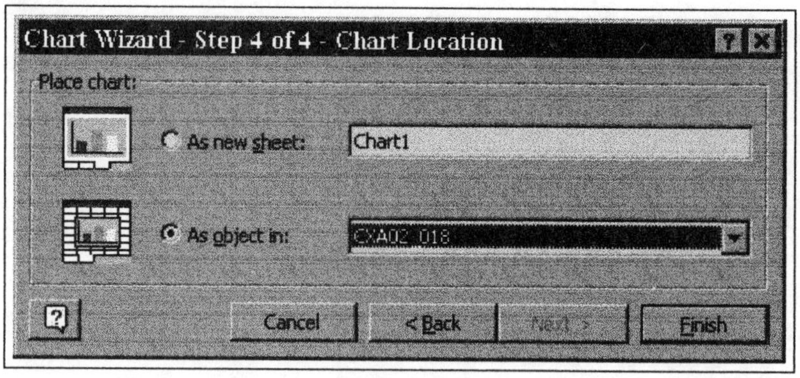

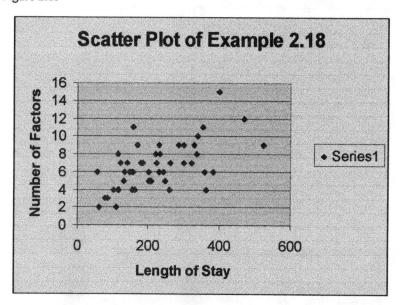

Figure 2.15

The scatter plot can also be used to create the time series plot discussed in *Statistics for Business and Economics*. When creating the scatter plot, the measure of time over which the data was collected should be used as the x-axis variable in the time series plot. All other steps are identical to that of the scatter plot discussed here.

2.3 Numerical Techniques in Excel

2.3.1 Measures of Center

Excel allows the user to create many descriptive measures of data through the use of the Descriptive Statistics data analysis. While Excel doesn't distinguish between the different types of numerical measures, we choose to follow the Statistics for Business and Economics text and look at the measures of center, spread, and relative standing one at a time. We begin with measures of center.

Example 2.4:   We use Statistics for Business and Economics Example 2.5 found on page 54 to illustrate the measures of center.

Calculate the sample mean for the R&D expenditure percentages of the 50 companies listed in Table 2.6.

Table 2.6

Company	Percentage	Company	Percentage	Company	Percentage
1	13.5	18	6.9	35	8.5
2	8.4	19	7.5	36	9.4
3	10.5	20	11.1	37	10.5
4	9	21	8.2	38	6.9
5	9.2	22	8	39	6.5
6	9.7	23	7.7	40	7.5
7	6.6	24	7.4	41	7.1
8	10.6	25	6.5	42	13.2
9	10.1	26	9.5	43	7.7
10	7.1	27	8.2	44	5.9
11	8	28	6.9	45	5.2
12	7.9	29	7.2	46	5.6
13	6.8	30	8.2	47	11.7
14	9.5	31	9.6	48	6
15	8.1	32	7.2	49	7.8
16	13.5	33	8.8	50	6.5
17	9.9	34	11.3		

Solution:

We must first retrieve a data set to work with. If you are using Excel97, **Open** the file CX02_005 For all other version, **Import** the CXA02_05.prn ASCII data set. Once the data is available, click on the **Tools** menu that appears at the top of the Excel worksheet. Select the **Data Analysis** option in the Tools menu and choose the **Descriptive Statistics** item (see Figure 2.16). Click **OK**.

Figure 2.16

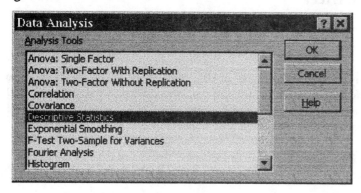

From the Descriptive Statistics menu, the user must specify the **Input Range**, the **Output Range**, and which statistics are desired. As with all Excel analyses, the Input Range should be the range of cells where the data set is located in the Excel worksheet. Either type or highlight with the mouse and enter the data set location for the Input Range (see Figure 2.17). The Output Range can either be a location within the current worksheet or a new Worksheet that you define. We opt to place the output in cell D1 of the current worksheet. Finally, the **Summary statistics** box needs to be **checked** to generate the measures of center that are desired. Click **OK**.

Figure 2.17

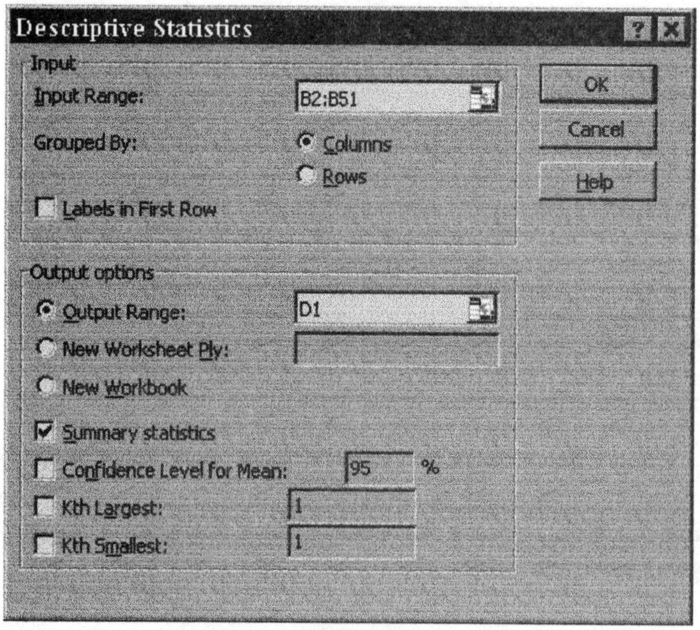

Excel calculates the three measures of center, mean, median, and mode for the data set of interest (see Table 2.7). The mean R&D expenditure for the 50 companies is reported to be 8.492 percent.

Table 2.7

Column1	
Mean	8.492
Standard Error	0.2801
Median	8.05
Mode	6.9
Standard Deviatior	1.980604
Sample Variance	3.922792
Kurtosis	0.419288
Skewness	0.854601
Range	8.3
Minimum	5.2
Maximum	13.5
Sum	424.6
Count	50

Calculating the measures of center for other data sets requires only changing the Input Range values in the Descriptive Statistics menu above.

2.3.2 Measures of Spread

The three measures of spread, range, standard deviation, and variance are found in the same manner as the measures of center above. We will use Example 2.10 from *Statistics for Business and Economics* to demonstrate.

Example 2.5: *Statistics for Business and Economics* Example 2.10 found on pages 66-67

Use the computer to find the sample variance s^2 and the sample standard deviation s for the 50 companies' percentage of revenues spent on R&D. The data is shown below in Table 2.8.

Table 2.8

Company	Percentage	Company	Percentage	Company	Percentage
1	13.5	18	6.9	35	8.5
2	8.4	19	7.5	36	9.4
3	10.5	20	11.1	37	10.5
4	9	21	8.2	38	6.9
5	9.2	22	8	39	6.5
6	9.7	23	7.7	40	7.5
7	6.6	24	7.4	41	7.1
8	10.6	25	6.5	42	13.2
9	10.1	26	9.5	43	7.7
10	7.1	27	8.2	44	5.9
11	8	28	6.9	45	5.2
12	7.9	29	7.2	46	5.6
13	6.8	30	8.2	47	11.7
14	9.5	31	9.6	48	6
15	8.1	32	7.2	49	7.8
16	13.5	33	8.8	50	6.5
17	9.9	34	11.3		

Solution:

We must first retrieve a data set to work with. If you are using Excel97, **Open** the file CX02_010. For all other version, **Import** the CXA02_10.prn ASCII data set. Once the data is available, click on the **Tools** menu that appears at the top of the Excel worksheet. Select the **Data Analysis** option in the Tools menu and choose the **Descriptive Statistics** item (see Figure 2.16). Click **OK**.

From the Descriptive Statistics menu, the user must specify the **Input Range**, the **Output Range**, and which statistics are desired. As with all Excel analyses, the Input Range should be the range of cells where the data set is located in the Excel worksheet. Either type or highlight with the mouse and enter the data set location for the Input Range (see Figure 2.17). The Output Range can either be a location within the current worksheet or a new Worksheet that you define. We opt to place the output in cell D1 of the current worksheet. Finally, the **Summary statistics** box needs to be **checked** to generate the measures of center that are desired. Click **OK**.

Excel calculates the three measures of spread, range, standard deviation, and variance for the data set of interest (see Table 2.9). The sample variance for the R&D expenditure of the 50 companies is reported to be 3.922791837 and the sample standard deviation is 1.980603907 percent.

Table 2.9

Column1	
Mean	8.492
Standard Error	0.2801
Median	8.05
Mode	6.9
Standard Deviation	1.980604
Sample Variance	3.922792
Kurtosis	0.419288
Skewness	0.854601
Range	8.3
Minimum	5.2
Maximum	13.5
Sum	424.6
Count	50

Calculating the measures of spread for other data sets requires only changing the Input Range values in the Descriptive Statistics menu above.

2.3.3 Measure of Relative Standing

Excel allows the user to calculate the two measures of relative standing, percentiles and z-scores through the use of two of it's many functions. We first look at how Excel calculates percentiles.

Example 2.6: Statistics for Business and Economics Example 2.10 found on pages 66-67

Use the data from Example 2.10 to calculate the 20th percentile of the R&D percentages.

Solution:

We must first retrieve a data set to work with. If you are using Excel97, **Open** the file CX02_010. For all other version, Import the CXA02_10.prn ASCII data set. Once the data is available, click the f_x icon at the top of the Excel worksheet. Choose the **Statistical Function Category** and cursor down until you reach the function name **PERCENTILE** (see Figure 2.18). The PERCENTILE function has the form:

PERCENTILE(array,k)

where **array** represents the location of the data set that you want to find the percentile for, and
      k is a number between 0 and 1 that represents the percentile that is desired.

Figure 2.18

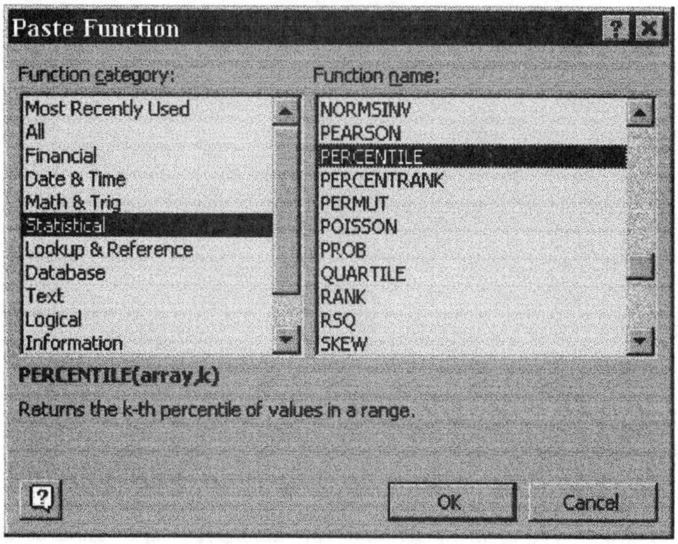

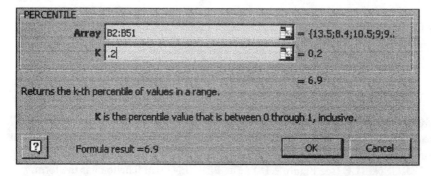

For this example, the 50 R&D percentages are located in column B in rows 2 through 51. We assign the **Array** location to be B2:B51 (see Figure 2.19). We also assign the value of **K** to be .20 representing the 20th percentile. Click **OK**.

Figure 2.19

Excel returns a value of 6.9. We interpret that 6.9 represents the 20th percentile of the 50 R&D percentages in our data set. By changing the data set and the value of K, we can find percentiles for any group of data.

The second measure of relative standing is the z-score. Again, we turn in Excel to a function that will allow the user to calculate values for a z-score. For purposes of illustration, we will again use the data from Example 2.10 to find a z-value.

Example 2.7:   Statistics for Business and Economics Example 2.10 found on pages 66-67

Use the 50 R&D percentages to find the z-score for an R&D percentage of 10%.

Solution:

We must first retrieve a data set to work with. If you are using Excel97, **Open** the file CX02_010. For all other version, **Import** the CXA02_10.prn ASCII data set. Once the data is available, click the f_x **icon** at the top of the Excel worksheet. Choose the **Statistical Function Category** and cursor down until you reach the function name **STANDARDIZE** (see Figure 2.20). The STANDARDIZE function has the form:

STANDARDIZE (x, mean, standard_dev)

where   **x** represents the value that you wish to determine the z-score for,
   mean represents the mean of the data set that you want to find the z-score for, and
   standard deviation represents the standard deviation of the data set that you want to find the
         z-score for.

Figure 2.20

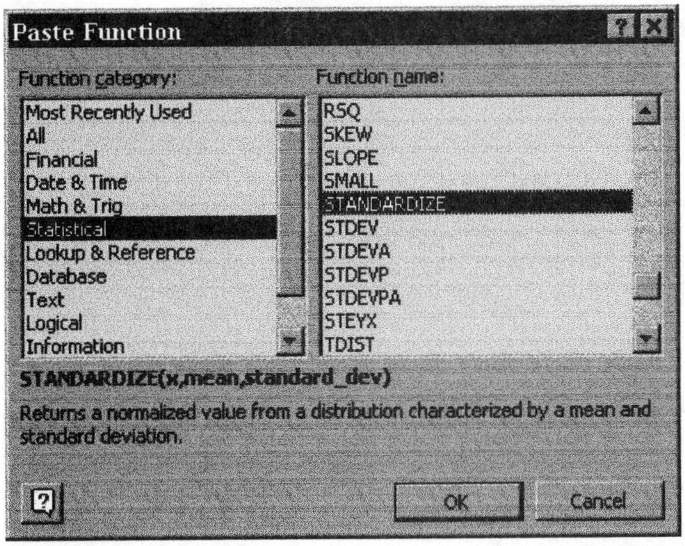

For this example, we use the value of 10 as our choice for **X** in the STANDARDIZE function (see Figure 2.21). From the work we did on Example 2.10, we know to use a value of 8.492 for the **mean** and a value of 1.980603907 for the **standard deviation**. Click **OK**.

Figure 2.21

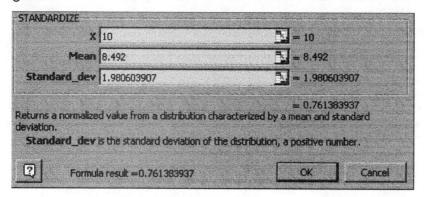

Excel returns a value of 0.762383937. We make the interpretation that an **R&D** percentage of 10% would fall approximately .76 standard deviations above the mean **R&D** percentage of the 50 companies. By changing the values of X, Mean, and Standard Deviation, we can find z-scores for a wide variety of situations.

Chapter 3
Probability

3.1 Introduction

Chapter 3 introduces the topic of probability to the reader. No data analysis using Microsoft Excel® is necessary in Chapter 3.

Chapter 4
Discrete Random Variables

4.1 Introduction

Chapter 4 introduces the two types of random variables, discrete and continuous, and discusses the discrete random variables in detail. Two discrete random variables, the binomial and poisson, are introduced and discussed in sections 4.4 and 4.5, respectively. The text introduces two main methods of working with both the binomial and poisson random variables. The first is to use their corresponding probability formulas (given in the text) to calculate probabilities associated with the random variables. The second is to use the probability tables reproduced in the appendix of the text. These tables are designed to give cumulative probabilities for specific binomial and poisson distributions.

Through the use of it's statistical functions, Excel can be used to find both individual and cumulative probabilities for both the binomial and poisson random variables. Excel can be used in place of either the formula or table methods mentioned above. The probability that the random variable is exactly equal to a specific number (e.g. the value 4) is referred to as an individual probability while the cumulative probability is the probability that the random variable is less than or equal to the specified value (e.g. less than or equal to 4). In the case of the binomial and poisson probability, the cumulative probability for the value 4 is equal to the sum of the individual probabilities of the values 0, 1, 2, 3, and 4. Through it's various options, Excel allows the user to determine which type of probability, individual or cumulative, to calculate.

The following examples from Statistics for Business and Economics are solved with Microsoft Excel® in this chapter:

Excel Companion		Statistics for Business and Economics	
Example	Page	SBE Example	SBE Page
4.1	60	4.11	186
4.2	63	4.12	191

4.2 Calculating Binomial Probabilities

Excel calculates both the individual and cumulative binomial probabilities through the BINOMDIST function. To use this function, you must first point and click the mouse on the function icon, f_x, in the icon bar at the top of the Excel worksheet. Next, click on the **Statistical Function Category** in the list given by Excel. Finally, choose the **BINOMDIST** function name given in the list provided. Click on **OK** (see Figure 4.1). This allows use of the binomial function provided by Excel.

Figure 4.1

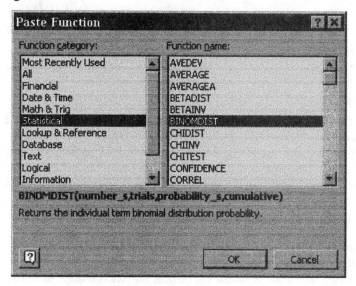

The binomial function requires the user to input the information in the following format:

BINOMDIST(number_s, trials, probability_s, cumulative)

where   **number_s** is the number of successes that is to be used in the probability calculation,
        trials is the number of trials in the binomial experiment being analyzed,
        probability_s is the probability of a success, p, and
        cumulative is either the word TRUE or FALSE. TRUE indicates that a cumulative
             probability is desired while FALSE indicates and individual probability is desired

Example 4.1:   As an example, we turn to Example 4.11 from *Statistics for Business and Economics*
            found on page 186 of the text.

Suppose a poll of 20 employees is taken in a large company. The purpose is to determine x, the number
who favor unionization. Suppose that 60% of all the company's employees favor unionization.

       a.   Find the mean and standard deviation of x.
       b.   Find the probability that x < 10.
       c.   Find the probability that x > 12.
       d.   Find the probability that x = 11.

Solution:

We can solve parts b-d using the BINOMDIST function within Excel. To do so, we must first identify that the number of trials in the above example is n = 20 employees. The probability of a success is p = .60.

b.   To find P(x < 10), we must use the cumulative probability P(x ≤ 9). In Excel, we use the BINOMDIST function as follows (see Figure 4.2):

        Enter **BINOMDIST(9, 20, .60, TRUE)** as shown in Figure 4.2. Click **OK**.

Figure 4.2

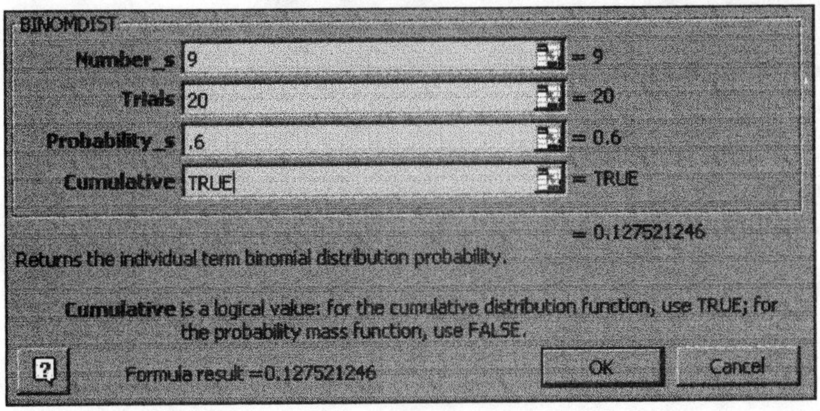

```
BINOMDIST
        Number_s  9                              = 9
          Trials  20                             = 20
    Probability_s  .6                            = 0.6
       Cumulative  TRUE                          = TRUE

                                                 = 0.127521246
Returns the individual term binomial distribution probability.

        Cumulative is a logical value: for the cumulative distribution function, use TRUE; for
                        the probability mass function, use FALSE.

   ?        Formula result = 0.127521246            OK        Cancel
```

        Excel returns the cumulative probability, P(x ≤ 9) = 0.127521. We can verify this result   using Table II of Appendix B (P(x ≤ 9) = .128).

c.   To find P(x > 12), we must use the cumulative probability P(x ≤ 12). In Excel, we use the BINOMDIST function as follows (see Figure 4.3):

        Enter **BINOMDIST(12, 20, .60, TRUE)** as shown in Figure 4.3. Click **OK**.

Figure 4.3

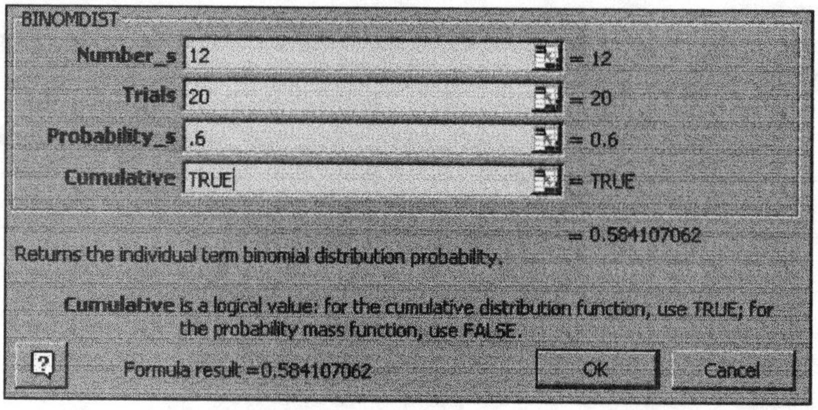

Excel returns the cumulative probability, $P(x \leq 12) = 0.584107$. We can verify this result using Table II of Appendix **B** ($P(x \leq 12) = .584$). We find the desired probability using $P(x > 12) = 1 - P(x \leq 12) = 1 - 0.584107 = 0.415893$.

d.   To find $P(x = 11)$, we must use the BINOMDIST function as follows (see Figure 4.4):

Enter **BINOMDIST(11, 20, .60, FALSE)** as shown in Figure 4.4. Click **OK**.

Figure 4.4

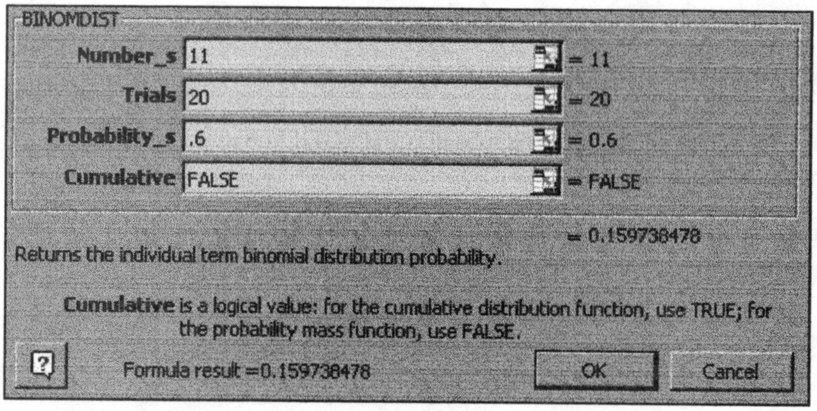

Excel returns the individual probability, $P(x = 11) = 0.159738$. We can verify this result using the binomial formula given in the text.

All other binomial probabilities can be found in a similar manner by changing **number_s**, **trials**, **probability_s**, and **cumulative** to the necessary values and allowing Excel to compute the desired probabilities.

4.3 Calculating Poisson Probabilities

Excel calculates both the individual and cumulative poisson probabilities through the POISSON function. To use this function, you must first point and click the mouse on the function icon, f_x, in the icon bar at the top of the Excel worksheet. Next, click on the **Statistical Function Category** in the list given by Excel. Finally, choose the **POISSON** function name given in the list provided. Click on **OK** (see Figure 4.5). This allows use to use the Poisson function provided by Excel.

Figure 4.5

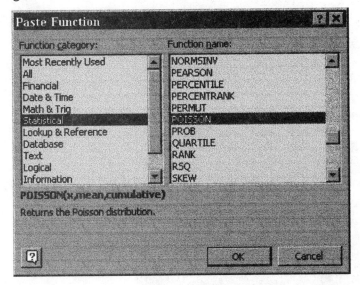

The Poisson function requires the user to input the information in the following format:

POISSON(x, mean, cumulative)

where   **x** is the number of interest that is to be used in the probability calculation
       mean is the known mean of the Poisson probability distribution
       cumulative is either the word TRUE or FALSE. TRUE indicates that a cumulative probability is
           desired while FALSE indicates and individual probability is desired.

Example 4.2:   As an example, we turn to Example 4.12 from *Statistics for Business and Economics* found on pages 191-192 of the text:

Suppose the number, x, of a company's employees who are absent on Monday's has (approximately) a Poisson probability distribution. Furthermore, assume that the average number of Monday absentees is 2.6.

a. Find the mean and standard deviation of x, the number of employees absent on Monday.
b. Find the probability that fewer than two employees are absent on a given Monday.
c. Find the probability that more than five employees are absent on a given Monday.
d. Find the probability that exactly five employees are absent on a given Monday.

Solution:

We can solve parts b-d using the POISSON function within Excel. To do so, we must first identify that the mean for this problem is 2.6 absentees.

b. To find $P(x < 2)$, we must use the cumulative probability $P(x \leq 1)$. In Excel, we use the POISSON function as follows (see Figure 4.6):

Enter **POISSON(1, 2.6, TRUE)** as shown if Figure 4.6. Click **OK**.

Figure 4.6

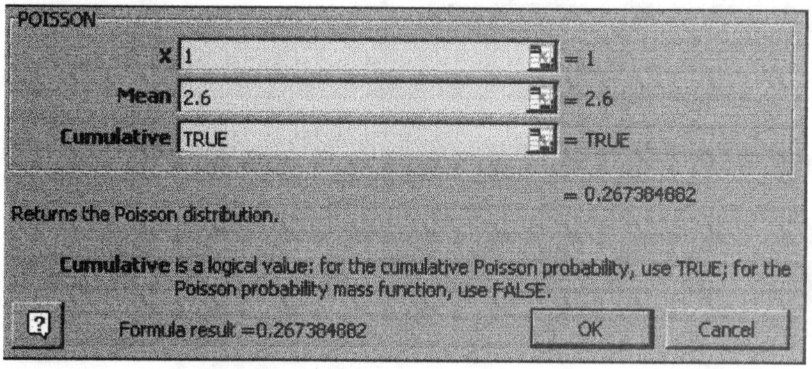

Excel returns the cumulative probability, $P(x \leq 1) = 0.267384882$. We can verify this result using Table III of Appendix B ($P(x \leq 1) = .267$.

c. To find $P(x > 5)$, we must use the cumulative probability $P(x \leq 5)$. In Excel, we use the POISSON function as follows (see Figure 4.7):

Enter **POISSON(5, 2.6, TRUE)** as shown in Figure 4.7. Click **OK**.

Figure 4.7

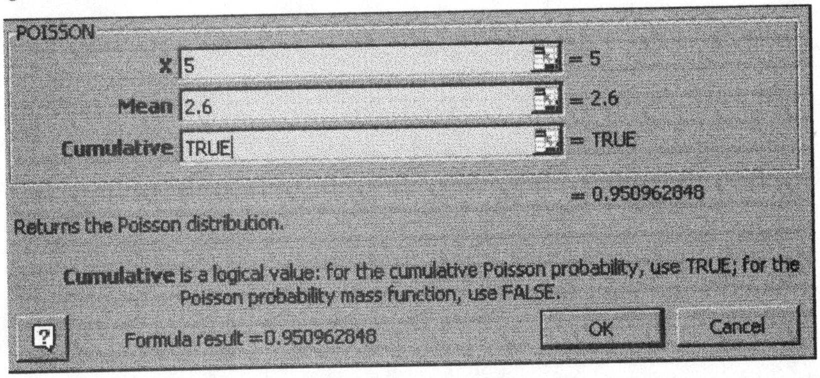

Excel returns the cumulative probability, $P(x \leq 5) = 0.950962848$. We can verify this result using Table III of Appendix B ($P(x \leq 5) = .951$. We find the desired probability using $P(x > 5) = 1 - P(x \leq 5) = 1 - 0.950962848 = 0.049037152$.

d. To find $P(x = 5)$, we must use the POISSON function as follows (see Figure 4.8):

Enter **POISSON(5, 2.6, False)** as shown in Figure 4.8. Click **OK**.

Figure 4.8

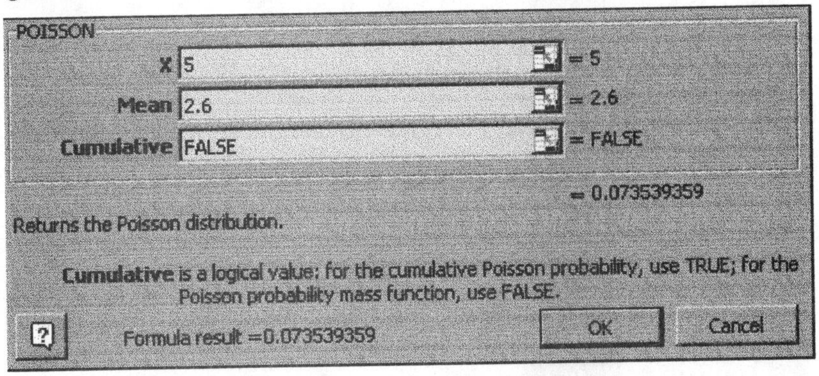

Excel returns the individual probability, $P(x = 5) = 0.073539359$ This can be verified using the Poisson formula given in the text.

All other Poisson probabilities can be found in a similar manner by changing **x**, **mean**, and **cumulative** to the necessary values and allowing Excel to compute the desired probabilities.

Chapter 5
Continuous Random Variables

5.1 Introduction

Chapter 5 introduces the second types of random variables, continuous random variables, and discusses the uniform, normal and exponential random variables in detail. The text introduces statistical tables as the best methods of working with the normal and the exponential random variables. The uniform random variable can be solved rather easily using simple mathematics. As we saw in Chapter 4, Excel can be used to duplicate the statistical tables presented in the text.

Through the use of it's statistical functions, Excel can be used to find cumulative probabilities for both the normal and exponential random variables. Excel can be used in place of the tables methods mentioned above. The following examples from *Statistics for Business and Economics* are solved with Microsoft Excel® in this chapter:

Excel Companion		Statistics for Business and Economics	
Example	Page	SBE Example	SBE Page
5.1	69	5.7	213
5.2	70	5.10	215
5.3	72	5.12	228

5.2 Calculating Normal Probabilities

Excel calculates cumulative normal probabilities through the NORMDIST function. To use this function, you must first point and click the mouse on the function icon, f_x, in the icon bar at the top of the Excel worksheet. Next, click on the **Statistical Function Category** in the list given by Excel. Finally, choose the **NORMDIST** function name given in the list provided. Click on **OK** (see Figure 5.1). This allows use of the normal function provided by Excel.

Figure 5.1

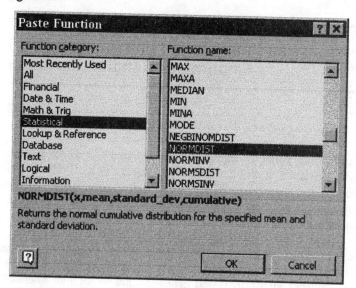

The NORMDIST function requires the user to input the information in the following format:

NORMDIST(x, mean, standard_dev, cumulative)

where   **x** is the number of the normal distribution to be used in the probability calculation,
        mean is the arithmetic mean of the normal distribution in question,
        standard_dev is the standard deviation of the normal distribution in question, and
        cumulative is the word TRUE. TRUE indicates that a cumulative probability is desired.

In addition to the NORMDIST function, Excel also offers the NORMINV function. The NORMINV function is useful when a specific value of the normal distribution is desired given some associated probability within the distribution (see Figure 5.2).

Figure 5.2

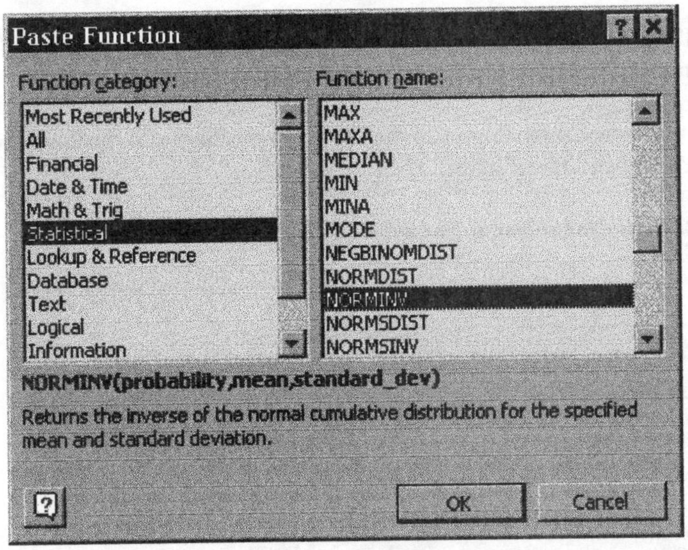

The NORMINV function requires the user to input the information in the following format:

NORMDIST(probability, mean, standard_dev)

where **probability** is the cumulative probability that is of interest,
       mean is the arithmetic mean of the normal distribution in question, and
       standard_dev is the standard deviation of the normal distribution in question.

The NORMDIST function can be illustrated with the following example.

Example 5.1: We use Example 5.7 from *Statistics for Business and Economics* found on pages 213-214 in the text:

Suppose an automobile manufacturer introduces a new model that has an advertised mean in-city mileage of 27 miles per gallon. Although such advertisements seldom report in any measure of variability, suppose you write the manufacturer for the details of the test, and find that the standard deviation is 3 miles per gallon. This information leads you to formulate a probability model for the random variable x, the in-city mileage for this car model. You believe that the probability distribution of x can be approximated by a normal distribution with a mean of 27 and a standard deviation of 3.

a.   If you were to buy this model of automobile, what is the probability that you would purchase one that averages less than 20 miles per gallon for in-city driving? In other words, find $P(x < 20)$.

Solution:

We can solve part a using the NORMDIST function within Excel. To do so, we must first identify that the mean and standard deviation of this normal distribution are 27 and 3, respectively.

a.   To find P(x < 20), we must use the cumulative probability NORMDIST function. In Excel, we use the NORMDIST function as follows (see Figure 5.3):

Enter **NORMDIST(20, 27, 3, TRUE)** as shown if Figure 5.3. Click **OK**.

Figure 5.3

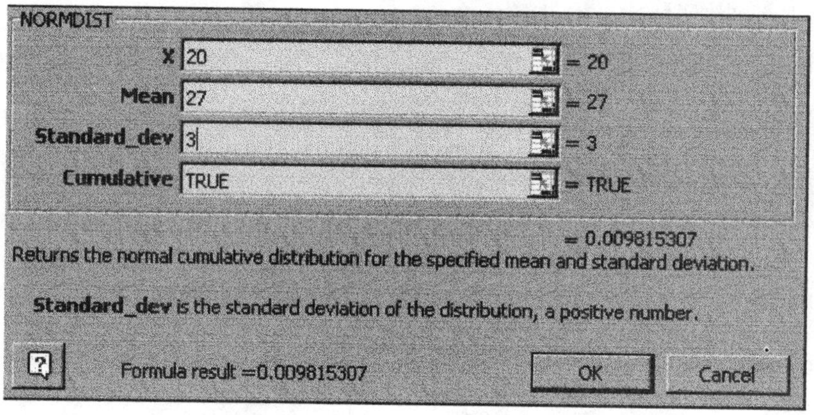

Excel returns the cumulative probability, P(x ≤ 20) = 0.009815307. We can verify this result using the z-score transformation and Table IV of Appendix B.

All other normal probabilities can be found in a similar manner by changing **x**, **mean**, **standard_dev**, and **cumulative** to the necessary values and allowing Excel to computer the desired probabilities.

The NORMINV function can be illustrated with the following example.

Example 5.2:   We use Example 5.10 from *Statistics for Business and Economics* found on pages 215-216 in the text:

Suppose a paint manufacturer has a daily production, x, that is normally distributed with a mean of 100,000 gallons and a standard deviation of 10,000 gallons. Management wants to create an incentive bonus for the production crew when the daily production exceeds the 90th percentile of the distribution, in hopes that the crew will, in turn, become more productive. At what level of production should management pay the incentive bonus?

Solution:

We can solve this question using the NORMINV function within Excel. To do so, we must first identify that the mean and standard deviation of this normal distribution are 100,000 and 10,000, respectively. In addition, we need to identify the cumulative probability of interest to the paint manufacturer. Because the 90th percentile is desired, we will use a cumulative probability of .90.

In Excel, we use the NORMINV function as follows (see Figure 5.4):

Enter **NORMINV(.90, 100,000, 10,000)** as shown in Figure 5.4. Click **OK**.

Figure 5.4

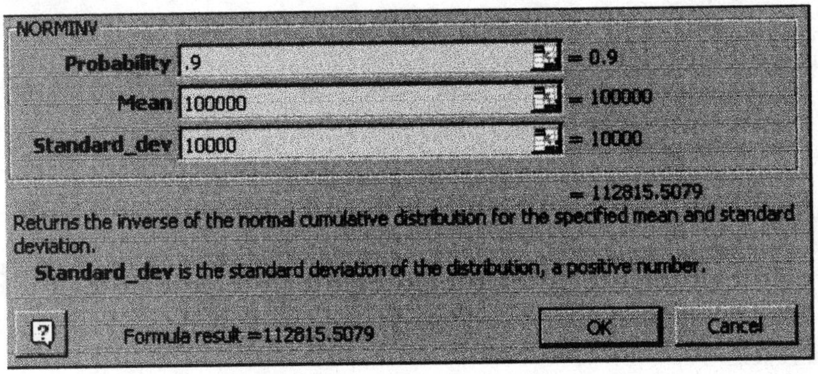

Excel returns the desired production level of 112,815 gallons. We can verify this result using the normal procedures discussed in the text and Table IV of Appendix B.

All other values within normal distributions can be found in a similar manner by changing **probability**, **mean**, and **standard_dev** to the necessary values and allowing Excel to calculate the desired point of interest.

5.3 Calculating Exponential Probabilities

Excel calculates cumulative exponential probabilities using the EXPONDIST function. To use this function, you must first point and click the mouse on the function icon, f_x, in the icon bar at the top of the Excel worksheet. Next, click on the **Statistical Function Category** in the list given by Excel. Finally, choose the **EXPONDIST** function name given in the list provided. Click on **OK** (see Figure 5.5). This allows use to use the exponential function provided by Excel.

Figure 5.5

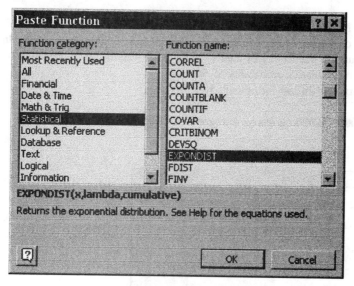

The exponential function requires the user to input the information in the following format:

EXPONDIST(x, lambda, cumulative)

where   **x** is the number of interest that is to be used in the probability calculation,
          lambda is $1/\mu$, where μ is the known value of the exponential mean,
          cumulative is the word TRUE. TRUE indicates that a cumulative probability is desired.

Example 5.3:   We use Example 5.12 from *Statistics for Business and Economics* found on page 228 in the text:

Suppose the length of time (in days) between sales for an automobile salesperson is modeled as an exponential distribution with l = .5. What is the probability the salesperson goes more than 5 days without a sale?

Solution:

We can solve this problem using the EXPONDIST function within Excel. To do so, we must first identify that the lambda value for this problem is 0.5.

To find P(x < 5), we must use the cumulative probability P(x ≤ 5). In Excel, we use the EXPONDIST function as follows (see Figure 5.6):

Enter **EXPONDIST(5, 0.5, TRUE)** as shown in Figure 5.6. Click **OK**.

Figure 5.6

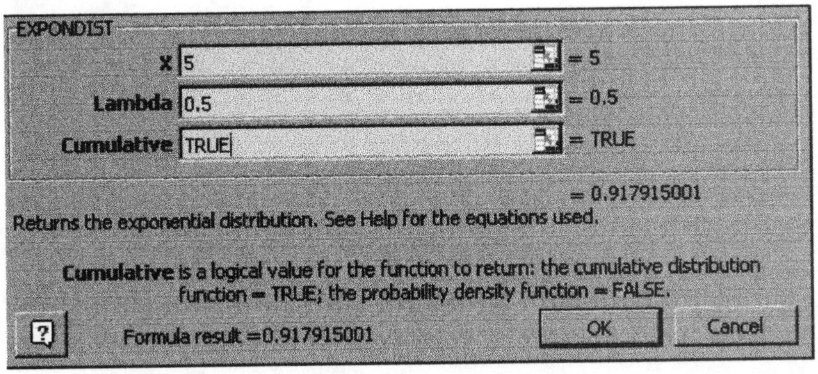

Excel returns the cumulative probability, $P(x \leq 5) = 0.917915001$. The probability that we desire is $P(x > 5) = 1 - P(x \leq 5) = 1 - 0.917915001 = .082084999$. We can verify this result using Table V of Appendix B $(P(x > 5) = .082085$.

All other exponential probabilities can be found in a similar manner by changing **x**, **lambda**, and **cumulative** to the necessary values and allowing Excel to compute the desired probabilities.

Chapter 6
Sampling Distributions

6.1 Introduction

Chapter 6 introduces the topic of sampling distributions to the reader. Microsoft Excel ® can be used when working with the sampling distribution of the sample mean covered in Section 6.3. Refer to the NORMDIST function discussed in chapter 5 of this manual for more information regarding this function.

Chapter 7
Inferences Based on a Single Sample:
Estimation with Confidence Intervals

7.1 Introduction

Chapter 7 introduces the reader to estimating population parameters with confidence intervals. Two parameters, the population mean and the population proportion, are studied in the chapter. The reader is also introduced to the topic of sample size determination, as it follows very nicely from the estimation material presented.

Excel allows for calculations of the confidence intervals when estimating population means, but provides no support when working with population proportions. For this reason, we limit our discussion in this chapter to estimating population means. From the material covered in *Statistics for Business and Economics*, it should be obvious that a separate estimation procedure is necessary for both the large sample and small sample estimations of a population mean. Excel gives methods for both cases, but does not label them very clearly. We examine both methods below.

The Descriptive Statistics analysis conducted by Excel calculates the summary statistics that we saw in Chapter 2. In addition, it allows the user to specify that a confidence interval be calculated for a population mean. The user can specify the level of confidence that is desired for this interval as a percentage between 0% and 100%. Excel provides the familiar descriptive statistics output with a single value given as the confidence interval. This value should be used as the number to add and subtract from the calculated sample mean to find the lower and upper endpoints of the confidence interval.

At first glance, the Descriptive Statistics analysis appears to be all that is needed to calculate a confidence interval for a population mean. The calculations used by Excel in this analysis utilize the t distribution discussed in the text. While this method works well with small samples, it is not appropriate for large sample estimation. In the large sample cases, the Descriptive Statistics analysis must be used in conjunction with the CONFIDENCE function that we discuss below.

The following examples from *Statistics for Business and Economics* are solved with Microsoft Excel® in this chapter:

Excel Companion		Statistics for Business and Economics	
Example	**Page**	**SBE Example**	**SBE Page**
7.1	78	7.1	273
7.2	81	7.2	282

7.2 Large Sample Estimation of a Population Mean

To estimate a population mean from a large sample, we must use Excel's Descriptive Statistics analysis as mentioned above. However, we use the descriptive statistics from this analysis so that we can calculate the mean, standard deviation, and sample size from the large sample of data that has been collected. We then take those values and use the CONFIDENCE function to calculate the large sample value that will lead to the upper and lower endpoints of the confidence interval for the population mean. We illustrate with the following example.

Example 7.1:   We use Example 7.1 from *Statistics for Business and Economics* found on pages 273-274 of the text.

Unoccupied seats on flights cause airlines to lose revenue. Suppose a large airline wants to estimate its average number of unoccupied seats per flight over the past year. To accomplish this, the records of 225 flights are randomly selected, and the number of unoccupied seats is noted for each of the sampled flights. The data is contained in Excel file CX07_001 (or ASCII file CXA07_01.prn). Estimate μ, the mean number of unoccupied seats per flight during the past year using a 90% confidence interval.

Solution:

Open the file containing the data set to create an Excel worksheet. The first step in this analysis will be to find the summary statistics necessary for the interval calculation. To do this, we must first click on the **Tools** menu found at the top of the Excel worksheet. Choose the **Data Analysis** option within the Tools menu. Choose the **Descriptive Statistics** option from within the Data Analysis menu (see Figure 7.1). Click **OK**.

Figure 7.1

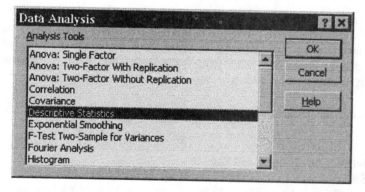

You should now be in the Descriptive Statistics menu. Enter the location of the data set in the **Input Range** cell of this menu (see Figure 7.2). Specify where the output of the calculations should be placed by specifying a new worksheet (New Worksheet Ply) or a location within the current worksheet (**Output Range**). Make sure to check the **Summary Statistics** box on this menu. We have also checked the **Confidence Level for Mean** box to illustrate that the results calculated by Excel correspond to the small sample estimation work covered in the next section of this manual. We have also entered the number **90** to represent the 90% level of confidence that is desired in this example Ordinarily, the Summary Statistics box is the only one that should be checked when working with a large sample. Click **OK**.

Excel returns the descriptive statistics shown in Table 7.1. We will use the values of the mean, standard deviation, and count from this output.

Figure 7.2

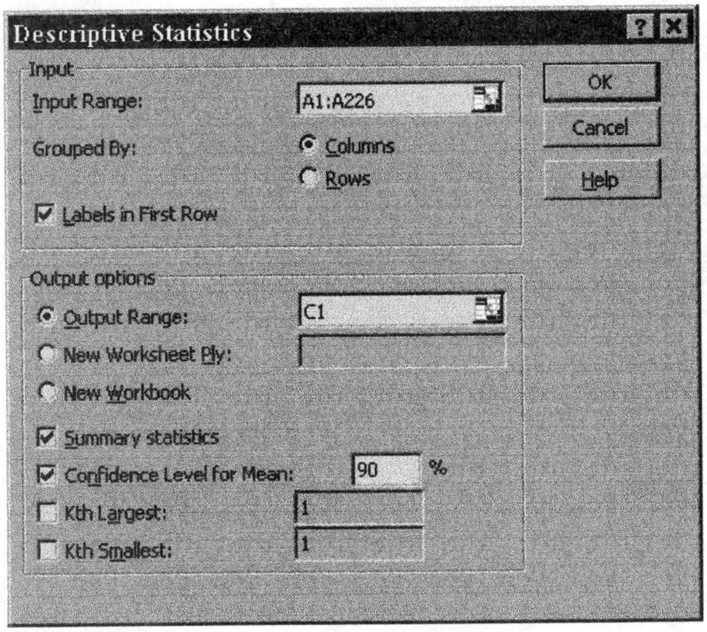

Table 7.1

Unoccupied Seats	
Mean	11.6
Standard Error	0.27342623
Median	12
Mode	14
Standard Deviation	4.10139349
Sample Variance	16.8214286
Kurtosis	0.56681088
Skewness	-0.2671597
Range	18
Minimum	2
Maximum	20
Sum	2610
Count	225
Confidence Level(90.0%)	0.45161354

To estimate a population mean from a large sample, we must click on the Function icon, f_x, at the top of the Excel worksheet. We choose the **STATISTICAL** function category from within the Function menu and the **CONFIDENCE** Function name from the list provided (see Figure 7.3). Click **OK**.

Figure 7.3

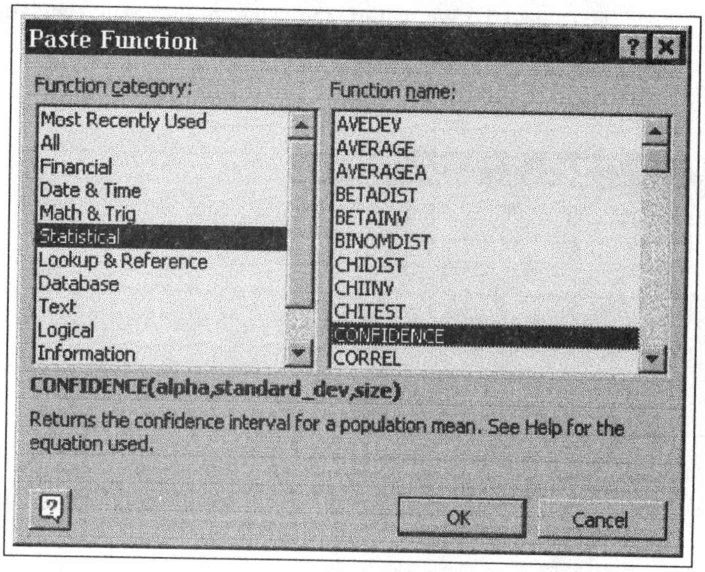

The CONFIDENCE function has the form:

CONFIDENCE(alpha, standard_dev, size)

where   **alpha** represents the error associated with your confidence interval (i.e., .10 when a 90% interval is
            desired),
        standard_dev is the standard deviation of the sampled data, and
        size is the sample size of the data collected.

For this example, we use an alpha of **.10**, a standard deviation of **4.10139** (from the descriptive statistics
output), and a size of **225** (also from the descriptive statistics output). We type these values in their
appropriate locations in the CONFIDENCE function (see Figure 7.4) and click **OK**.

Figure 7.4

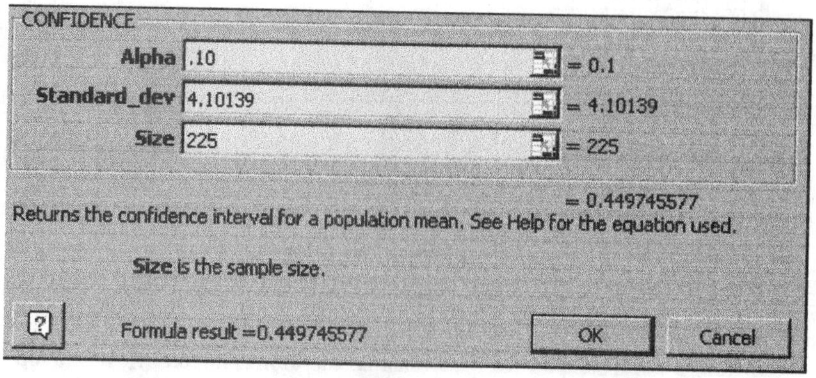

The CONFIDENCE function returns a value of 0.4497. This is the value that is added and subtracted from the sample mean that was calculated on the descriptive statistics output. We find the endpoints of the confidence interval in the following manner:

(sample mean) $\pm$ (value from CONFIDENCE function)

In this example: $11.6 \pm .4497$

The 90% confidence interval is (11.1503, 12.0497).

If the values of the sample standard deviation and sample size are known, the CONFIDENCE function can be used without conducting a descriptive analysis of the data. Simply type in the appropriate values as was done above and click OK.

It is worthwhile to compare the value calculated from the CONFIDENCE function (.4497) to the 90% confidence value given by the descriptive statistics output of Table 7.1 (.4516) to understand the difference between the two values. The difference is the result of these two methods utilizing different probability distributions in their calculations. The descriptive output always uses the t distribution in it's calculation while the CONFIDENCE function always uses the z distribution. For this example, the large sample analysis is more appropriate, so we must use the results of the CONFIDENCE function. The key is for the user to be aware of which distribution is correct and to use the appropriate Excel method. We look at a small sample example next.

7.3 Small Sample Estimation of a Population Mean

From an Excel perspective, the small sample estimation of a population mean is far easier than the large sample estimation discussed in the last section. The Descriptive Statistics output from Excel is all that is needed in the small sample case. Since it uses the t distribution in the calculations of the confidence interval value, it should be used whenever the sample size is considered small. The next example illustrates one use of this method.

Example 7.2:   We use Example 7.2 from *Statistics for Business and Economics* found on pages 282-283.

Some quality control experiments require destructive sampling (i.e., the test to determine whether the item is defective destroys the item) in order to measure some particular characteristic of the product. The cost of destructive sampling often dictates small samples. For example, suppose a manufacturer of printers for personal computers wishes to estimate the mean number of characters printed before the printhead fails. Suppose the printer manufacturer tests $n = 15$ randomly selected printheads and records the number of characters printed until failure of each. These 15 measurements (in millions of characters) are listed in Table 7.2 below. Form a 99% confidence interval for the mean number of characters printed before the printhead fails.

Table 7.2

Number of Characters (In Millions)			
1.13	1.32	1.18	1.25
1.36	1.33	0.92	1.48
1.2	1.43	1.07	1.29
1.55	0.85	1.22	

Solution:

Open the file containing the data set (Excel97 file CX07_002 or ASCII file CX07_02.prn) to create an Excel worksheet. The first step is to click on the **Tools** menu found at the top of the Excel worksheet. Choose the **Data Analysis** option within the Tools menu. Choose the **Descriptive Statistics** option from within the Data Analysis menu (see Figure 7.5). Click **OK**.

Figure 7.5

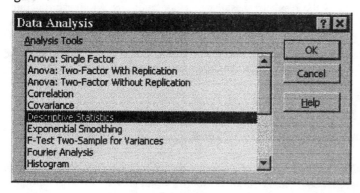

You should now be in the Descriptive Statistics menu. Enter the location of the data set in the **Input Range** cell of this menu (see Figure 7.6). Specify where the output of the calculations should be placed by specifying a new worksheet (New Worksheet Ply) or a location within the current worksheet (**Output Range**). Make sure to check the **Summary Statistics** box on this menu. Also check the **Confidence Level for Mean** box and enter the value 99 to form the 99% confidence interval. Click **OK**.

Figure 7.6

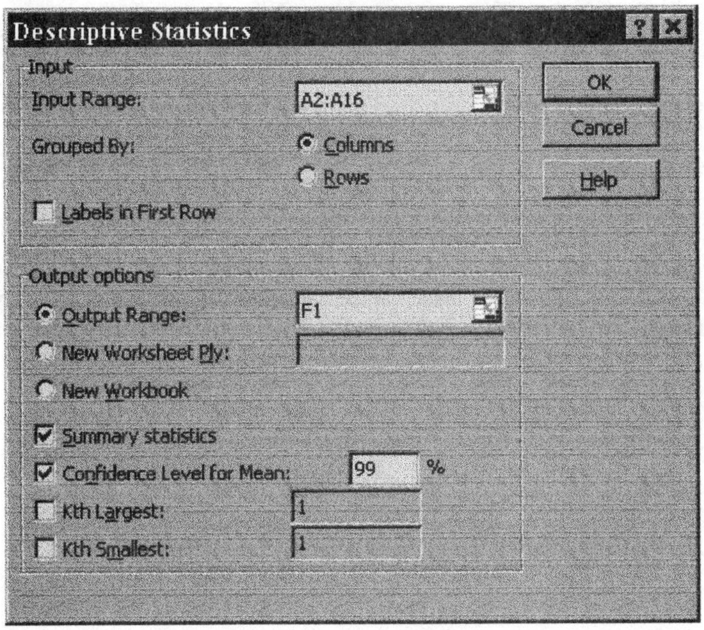

Table 7.3

Column1	
Mean	1.238667
Standard Error	0.049875
Median	1.25
Mode	#N/A
Standard Deviation	0.193164
Sample Variance	0.037312
Kurtosis	0.063636
Skewness	-0.49126
Range	0.7
Minimum	0.85
Maximum	1.55
Sum	18.58
Count	15
Confidence Level(99.0%)	0.14847

Excel returns the standard summary output of the data set as well as the 99% confidence level value (see Table 7.3). This value can be used to calculate the 99% confidence interval for the population mean as follows:

(Sample Mean) $\pm$ (Confidence Level value)

In our example, the confidence interval becomes:

1.239 $\pm$ 0.1485   or from 1.0905 to 1.3875 million characters.

All other small sample confidence intervals for a population mean can be calculated in a similar manner by changing the input range of the data and the level of confidence desired.

Chapter 8
Inferences Based on a Single Sample:
Tests of Hypothesis

8.1 Introduction

Chapter 8 introduces the reader to the concepts of hypothesis testing. The general theory and concepts of the test of hypothesis are then examined for inferences based on a single sample. Tests for both a single population mean and a single population proportion are discussed in Chapter 8. In addition, the observed significance level of a test of hypothesis is explained and demonstrated in several examples.

Excel does not provide any specific menus or functions that allow for the test of hypothesis procedure to be calculated. However, several of the menus and functions that we have seen earlier in this manual can be used to simplify the calculations involved in the test of hypothesis. Our approach here is to provide the most efficient method within Excel of calculating the numbers that will simplify the test of hypothesis procedure discussed in the text.

We discuss these procedures by considering the two main components in which calculations are involved. First, we use the Descriptive Statistics menu to aid in the calculation of the test statistic of the test of hypothesis. Second, we use the NORMSDIST and TDIST functions within Excel to calculate the appropriate p-value for the test of hypothesis. The following examples from *Statistics for Business and Economics* are solved with Microsoft Excel® in this chapter:

Excel Companion		Statistics for Business and Economics	
Example	Page	SBE Example	SBE Page
8.1	85	8.4	334
8.2	88	8.5	340
8.3	91	8.4	334
8.4	93	8.5	340

8.2 Calculating Test Statistics Within Excel

The easiest method to calculate the value of the test statistic in a test of hypothesis for a population mean is to use Excel to generate the summary statistics for a data set and to use the results to calculate the test statistic in the formulas given in the text. We illustrate this method with two examples.

Example 8.1: We use Example 8.4 on page 334 of the *Statistics for Business and Economics* text.

Knowledge of the amount of time a patient occupies a hospital bed--called length of stay (LOS)--is important for allocating resources. At one hospital, the mean length of stay was determined to be 5 days. A hospital administrator believes the mean LOS may now be less than 5 days due to a newly adopted managed care system. To check this, the LOS's (in days) for 100 randomly selected hospital patients were recorded (see Table 8.1). Test the hypothesis that the true mean LOS at the hospital is less than 5 days.

Table 8.1:

Lengths of Stay for 100 Hospital Patients									
2	3	8	6	4	4	6	4	2	5
8	10	4	4	4	2	1	3	2	10
1	3	2	3	4	3	5	2	4	1
2	9	1	7	17	9	9	9	4	4
1	1	1	3	1	6	3	3	2	5
1	3	3	14	2	3	9	6	6	3
5	1	4	6	11	22	1	9	6	5
2	2	5	4	3	6	1	5	1	6
17	1	2	4	5	4	4	3	2	3
3	5	2	3	3	2	10	2	4	2

Solution:

The first step in the Excel analysis is to enter the data of Table 8.1 into an Excel worksheet. **Open** Excel97 file CX08_004 or import the ASCII file CXA08_04.prn into an Excel worksheet. Click on the **Tools** menu located at the top of the Excel worksheet. Choose the **Data Analysis** option from within the Tools menu. Choose the **Descriptive Statistics** option from within the Data Analysis menu (see Figure 8.1). Click **OK**.

Figure 8.1

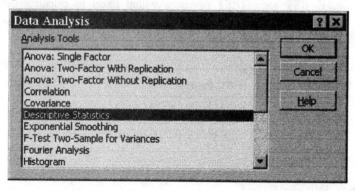

You should now be in the Descriptive Statistics menu. Enter the location of the data set in the **Input Range** cell of this menu (see Figure 8.2). Specify where the output of the calculations should be placed by specifying a new worksheet (New Worksheet Ply) or a location within the current worksheet (**Output Range**). Make sure to check the **Summary Statistics** box on this menu. Click **OK**.

Figure 8.2

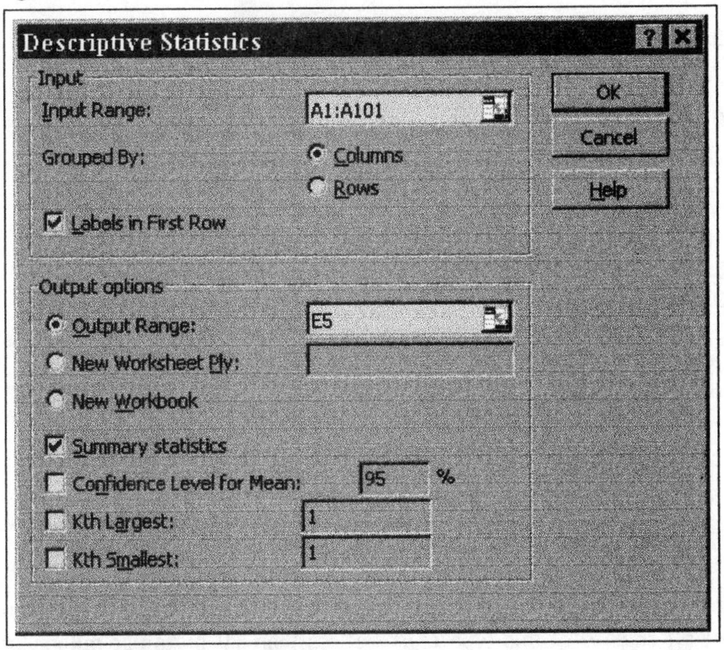

The resulting output is shown below in Table 8.2. The test statistic formula when testing a population mean requires a value for the mean, standard deviation, and sample size of the sample that is being analyzed. These three values can all be found in this printout and used to calculate the test statistic appropriate for the analysis. The test statistic is found as follows:

$$z = \frac{\bar{x} - \mu_0}{s/\sqrt{n}} = \frac{4.53 - 5}{3.6775/\sqrt{100}} = -1.278$$

This value can then be used to determine whether the null hypothesis can be rejected. Our purpose here is to demonstrate how Excel can be used to ease the calculation of this value. The observed significance level for this test will be found in the next section.

Table 8.2

Lengths of Stay for 100 Hospital Patients	
Mean	4.53
Standard Error	0.367754584
Median	4
Mode	3
Standard Deviation	3.677545844
Sample Variance	13.52434343
Kurtosis	6.278812991
Skewness	2.181620423
Range	21
Minimum	1
Maximum	22
Sum	453
Count	100

Example 8.2:   We use Example 8.5 found on page 340 of the *Statistics for Business and Economics* text.

A major car manufacturer wants to test a new engine to determine whether it meets new air pollution standards. The mean emission μ of all engines of this type must be less than 20 parts per million of carbon. Ten engines are manufactured for testing purposes, and the emission level of each is determined. The data are shown in Table 8.3 below. Do the data supply sufficient evidence to allow the manufacturer to conclude that this type of engine meets the pollution standard? Assume that the production process is stable and the manufacturer is willing to risk a Type I error with probability $\alpha = .01$.

Table 8.3

Emission Level of Engine
15.6
16.2
22.5
20.5
16.4
19.4
16.6
17.9
12.7
13.9

Solution:

As we saw in the last example, Excel can be used to create the summary statistics necessary for calculating the test statistic. The first step in the Excel analysis is to enter the data of Table 8.3 into an Excel worksheet. **Open** Excel97 file CX08_005 or import the ASCII file CXA08_05.prn into an Excel worksheet. Click on the **Tools** menu located at the top of the Excel worksheet. Choose the **Data Analysis** option from within the Tools menu. Choose the **Descriptive Statistics** option from within the Data Analysis menu (see Figure 8.3). Click **OK**.

Figure 8.3

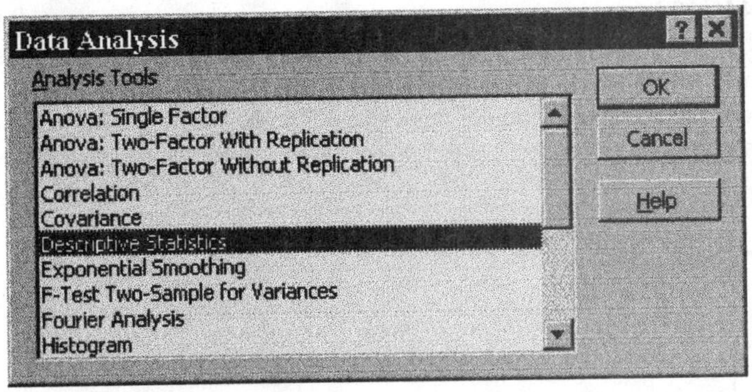

You should now be in the Descriptive Statistics menu. Enter the location of the data set in the **Input Range** cell of this menu (see Figure 8.4). Specify where the output of the calculations should be placed by specifying a new worksheet (New Worksheet Ply) or a location within the current worksheet (**Output Range**). Make sure to check the **Summary Statistics** box on this menu. Click **OK**.

Figure 8.4:

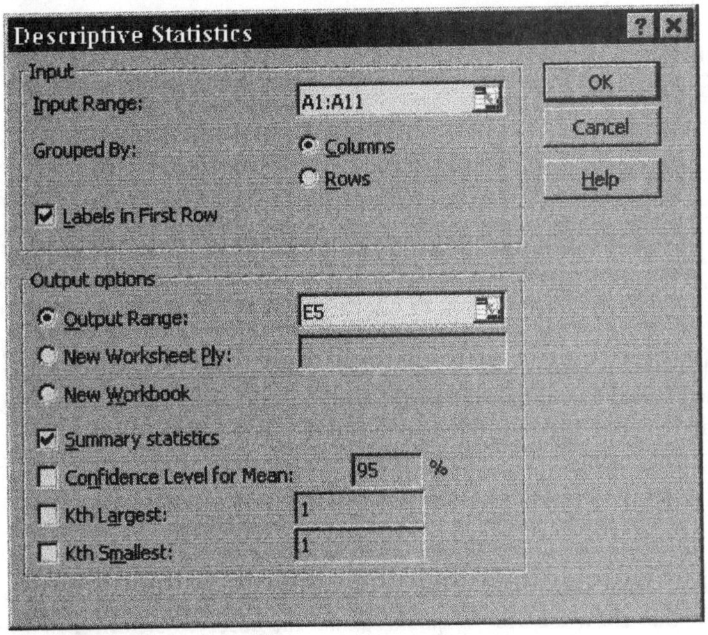

The resulting output is shown below in Table 8.4. The test statistic formula when testing a population mean requires a value for the mean, standard deviation, and sample size of the sample that is being analyzed. These three values can all be found in this Table 8.4 and used to calculate the test statistic appropriate for the analysis. The test statistic is found as follows:

$$z = \frac{\bar{x} - \mu_0}{s/\sqrt{n}} = \frac{17.17 - 20}{2.98144/\sqrt{10}} = -3.002$$

This value can then be used to determine whether the null hypothesis can be rejected. Our purpose here is to demonstrate how Excel can be used to ease the calculation of this value. The observed significance level for this test will be found in the next section.

Table 8.4:

Emission Level of Engine	
Mean	17.17
Standard Error	0.942814934
Median	16.5
Mode	#N/A
Standard Deviation	2.981442604
Sample Variance	8.889
Kurtosis	-0.26216874
Skewness	0.367473552
Range	9.8
Minimum	12.7
Maximum	22.5
Sum	171.7
Count	10

8.3 Calculating the P-value for a Test of Hypothesis

In the last section, we used Excel to calculate the value of the test statistic when conducting a test of hypothesis for a population mean. There are two methods of using this test statistic to make conclusions for the desired test. The first is to compare the test statistic to a critical value found in the appropriate statistical table in the text. This is the rejection region approach discussed in the *Statistics for Business and Economics* text. The second method is referred to as the observed significance, or p-value, approach that is also discussed in the text. The p-value approach involves determining how significant the calculated test statistic is in relation to the appropriate sampling distribution being used. This p-value is then compared to your defined Type I error tolerance to make the appropriate conclusion for the test of hypothesis. Please review the text to get further explanations concerning these two methods of making conclusions in a test of hypothesis.

Excel can be used to aid in conclusions made using the p-value approach. Excel provides two statistical functions, NORMSDIST and TDIST, that allow the user to quickly attain the observed significance level of the test. These functions must be used after a value of the test statistic has been calculated. Please refer to the Section 8.2 of this manual for information on using Excel to calculate the value of the test statistic necessary for use of these two functions.

8.3.1 Finding P-values for Large Sample Tests of Hypotheses

The Excel function that corresponds to the large sample test of hypothesis p-value calculation is the NORMSDIST function. We demonstrate using this function to calculate the test statistic with the following large sample example.

Example 8.3: Use the results of Example 8.1 (Example 8.4 in *Statistics for Business and Economics* found on pages 334-335) to find the observed significance level of the test. The data of this example is reproduced below in Table 8.5.

Table 8.5

Lengths of Stay for 100 Hospital Patients									
2	3	8	6	4	4	6	4	2	5
8	10	4	4	4	2	1	3	2	10
1	3	2	3	4	3	5	2	4	1
2	9	1	7	17	9	9	9	4	4
1	1	1	3	1	6	3	3	2	5
1	3	3	14	2	3	9	6	6	3
5	1	4	6	11	22	1	9	6	5
2	2	5	4	3	6	1	5	1	6
17	1	2	4	5	4	4	3	2	3
3	5	2	3	3	2	10	2	4	2

Solution:

We calculated a value of the test statistic ($z = -1.278$) in Example 8.1 when testing the hypotheses:

H_o: $\mu = 5$

H_a: $\mu < 5$

We now need to calculate the observed significance level for this large sample, lower-tail test of hypothesis. Excel provides the NORMSDIST statistical function as a means to finding the desired p-value for this problem.

Open any Excel worksheet and click on any cell within the worksheet. Click on the function icon, f_x, at the top of the Excel worksheet. Highlight the **Statistical** function from the list of function categories available on the Paste Function menu (see Figure 8.5). Scroll down the Function name list and highlight the **NORMSDIST** function from the choices provided. Click **OK**.

Figure 8.5

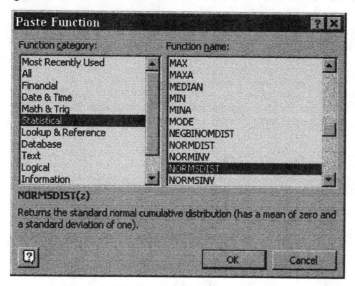

The NORMSDIST function requires the user to input information in the following format:

NORMSDIST(z)

   where **z** is the value of the test statistic calculated for the test of hypothesis to be conducted.

To find the p-value in this example, we need to enter the value of the test statistic, **z = -1.278**, into the NORMDIST Function (see Figure 8.6). Click **OK**.

Figure 8.6

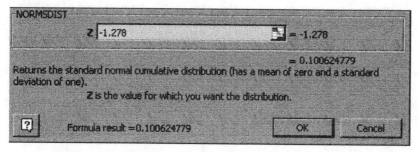

NORMDIST returns the formula result = 0.1006. This value represents the cumulative probability value of the standard normal distribution. Since we are conducting a lower tail test, this value also represents the p-value desired for this test of hypothesis problem. Compare this p-value to the one calculated in Example 8.4 *Statistics for Business and Economics* found on page 335 of the text.

The NORMSDIST function always returns the cumulative probability associated with the value of z that has been entered. The user must take care to ensure that the cumulative probability returned by Excel is, in fact, the desired p-value for the test being conducted. The cumulative probability will be correct if a lower tail test of hypothesis is desired, as was the case in the last example. If an upper tail test is conducted, subtract the cumulative probability derived from 1 to arrive at the desired p-value for the test. If a two-tailed test is desired, use a negative sign in front of the test statistic (even if a positive test statistic has been calculated) entered in the NORMSDIST function and double the cumulative probability derived to get the desired p-value. In short, the user needs to make sure that the p-value desired is found in the appropriate manner when using the NORMSDIST function within Excel.

8.3.2   Finding P-values for Small Sample Tests of Hypotheses

The Excel function that corresponds to the small sample test of hypothesis p-value calculation is the TDIST function. We demonstrate using this function to calculate a test statistic with the following small sample example.

Example 8.4:   Use the results of Example 8.2 (Example 8.5 in *Statistics for Business and Economics* found on page 340) to find the observed significance level of the test. The data of this example is reproduced below in Table 8.6.

Table 8.6

Emission Level of Engine
15.6
16.2
22.5
20.5
16.4
19.4
16.6
17.9
12.7
13.9

Solution:

We calculated a value of the test statistic ($z = -3.002$) in Example 8.2 when testing the hypotheses:

$$H_o: \mu = 20$$
$$H_a: \mu < 20$$

We need to calculate the observed significance level for this small sample, lower-tail test of hypothesis. Excel provides the TDIST statistical function as a means to finding the desired p-value of this problem.

Open any Excel worksheet and click on any cell within the worksheet. Click on the function icon, f_x, at the top of the Excel worksheet. Highlight the **Statistical** function from the list of function categories available on the Paste Function menu (see Figure 8.7). Scroll down the Function name list and highlight the **TDIST** function from the choices provided. Click **OK**.

Figure 8.7

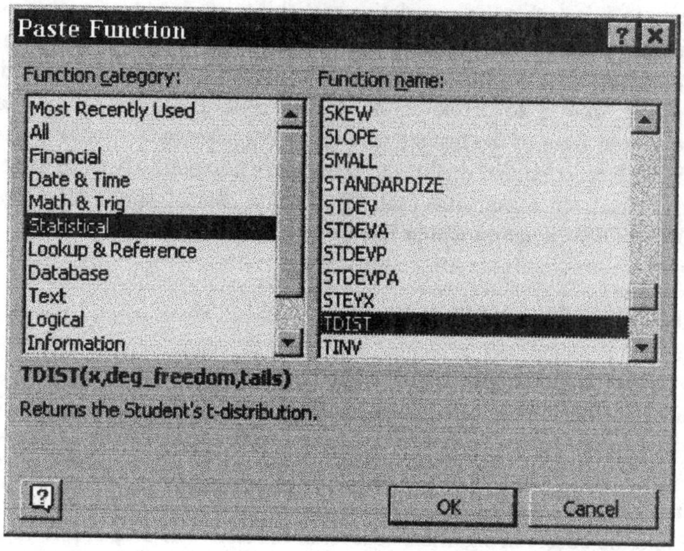

The TDIST function requires the user to input information in the following format:

TDIST(x, deg_freedom, tails)

where   **x** is the absolute value of the test statistic calculated for the test of hypothesis to be conducted,
        deg_freedom is the number of degrees of freedom for the small sample test, and
        tails is 1 or 2, the number of tails of the distribution that the test is considering.

In this example, with a sample of size n=10, a test statistic of t=-3.002, and a lower tail test, we use the TDIST as follows (see Figure 8.8):

Enter **TDIST(3.002, 9, 1)** as shown in Figure 8.8. Click **OK**.

Figure 8.8

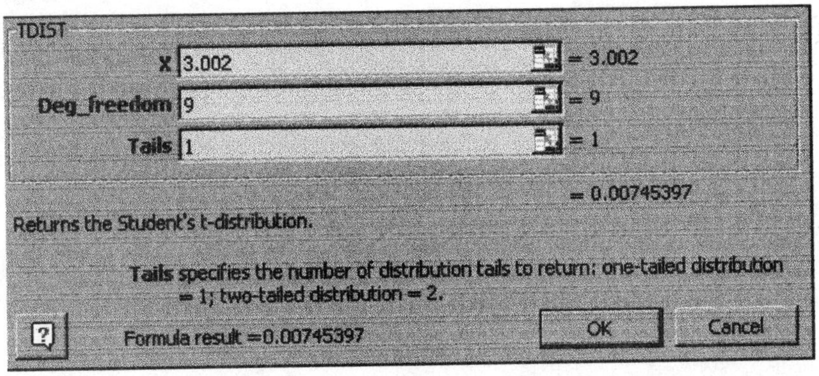

TDIST returns the formula result = 0.00745. This value is the desired p-value for this test of hypothesis. Compare this value to the one derived in Example 8.6 *of Statistics for Business and Economics* found on page 341 of the text.

When used correctly as shown above, the TDIST function always returns a formula result that corresponds to the desired p-value. It is important to remember to use the absolute value of the test statistic when using the TDIST function in EXCEL. The resulting formula value is easier to interpret than the corresponding value from the large sample NORMSDIST function since the value derived from the TDIST function is always the desired p-value. Make sure to understand how to use both the NORMSDIST and TDIST functions to insure that the correct p-value is always being calculated.

Chapter 9
Inferences Based on Two Samples:
Confidence Intervals and Tests of Hypothesis

9.1 Introduction

Chapter 9 introduces the reader to two sample problems using both the estimation and test of hypothesis techniques discussed in Chapters 7 and 8. Three types of parameters, population means, population proportions, and population variances, are studied in the chapter. The reader is also introduced to the topic of sample size determination, as it follows very nicely from the estimation material presented.

Excel offers more analytic choices for two sample problems than it does for the one sample problems of Chapters 7 and 8. Excel offers a test of hypothesis procedure for comparing two independent population means and a test of hypothesis procedure for comparing two population variances. While no specific analyses exists within Excel to estimate the independent samples difference in means confidence interval, the test of hypothesis procedure can be used to calculate the summary information necessary for the confidence interval calculations. The paired difference comparison of means presented in Chapter 9 can be estimated with the descriptive statistics analysis within Excel, but no testing procedure exists for this paired difference analysis. As we saw in Chapters 7 and 8, Excel does not offer any help with the proportion problems of Chapter 9. Our discussions in this chapter will be limited to using estimation procedures to compare two population means and to use testing procedures to compare population means and variances.

The following examples from *Statistics for Business and Economics* are solved with Microsoft Excel® in this chapter:

Excel Companion Example	Page	SBE Example	SBE Page
9.1	98	9.4	374
9.2	100	9.4	374
9.3	103	9.3	371
9.4	105	9.5	391
9.5	108	9.13	414

9.2 Comparing Population Means - Independent Samples

9.2.1 Confidence Intervals

Chapter 9 presents both the estimation and test of hypothesis procedures for comparing two independent population means. Excel provides two statistical analyses for testing the difference of two population means. The main difference between these two procedures is the relationship between the two population variances. Excel provides a procedure for both the equal and unequal population variance situations. As we have seen before in Excel, these procedures both rely on the t distribution in the calculation of p-values. Care must be taken by the user to make sure the correct p-value is found for the desired test of hypothesis. We demonstrate the various Excel options available in the examples presented.

Example 9.1:   We use Example 9.4 found on pages 374-376 of *Statistics for Business and Economics*.

Behavioral researchers have developed an index designed to measure managerial success. The index (measured on a 100-point scale) is based on the manager's length of time in the organization and his or her level within the firm; the higher the index, the more successful the manager. Suppose a researcher wants to compare the average success index for two groups of managers at a large manufacturing plant. Managers in group 1 engage in a high volume of interactions with people outside the manager's work unit. (Such interactions include phone and face-to-face meetings with customers and suppliers, outside meetings, and public relations work.)   Managers in group 2 rarely interact with people outside their work unit. Independent random samples of 12 and 15 managers are selected from groups 1 and 2, respectively, and the success index of each recorded. The results of the study are given in Table 9.1.

a.   Use the data in the table to estimate the true mean difference between the success indexes of managers in the two groups. Use a 95% confidence interval, and interpret the interval.

b.   What assumptions must be made in order that the estimate be valid? Are they reasonably satisfied?

Table 9.1

GROUP 1			GROUP 2		
65	78	68	62	53	68
66	53	63	42	36	56
58	60	69	52	46	48
70	71	63	53	43	50
			57	34	42

Solution:

The confidence interval analysis that is desired cannot be accomplished entirely within Excel. However, the Excel results found in the test of hypothesis analysis can be used to easily construct the desired confidence interval. That is the approach that we will take.

The first step is to **Open** data file CX09_004 or **Import** the ASCII data file CXA09_04.prn. From the main menu, we next click the **Tools** menu located at the top of the Excel worksheet. Select the **Data Analysis** option from within the tools menu (see Figure 9.1). It is here the user must make a decision. There are two test of hypothesis analyses that Excel allows the user to conduct. The user must know whether an equal or unequal variance analysis is appropriate. We refer you to the text for more information on this subject. For the purpose of this example, we believe the equal variance analysis is appropriate. We next highlight the **t-Test: Two-Sample Assuming Equal Variances** option from the Analysis Tools given in the Data Analysis menu. Click **OK**.

Figure 9.1

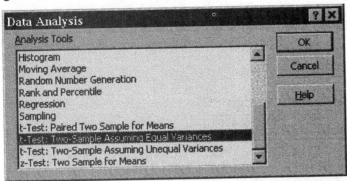

The user should now be at the t-Test menu for comparing population means (assuming equal population variances). As with all data analysis menus, the first step is to input the range of the data that is to be analyzed. Because this is a two sample problem, Excel specifies two separate locations for the input data (see Figure 9.2). Either **type** the location of the first sample or **click and drag** it's location for the Variable 1 Range and do the same for the second sample for the Variable 2 Range to input the data that you wish to compare. Enter a value of **0** for the Hypothesized Mean Difference and specify **.05** for the level of Alpha (since a 95% confidence interval was stated in the problem). Specify the appropriate location of the generated output by **checking** either the Output Range, New Worksheet Ply, or New Workbook option in the Output options section of the menu. Click **OK**.

Figure 9.2

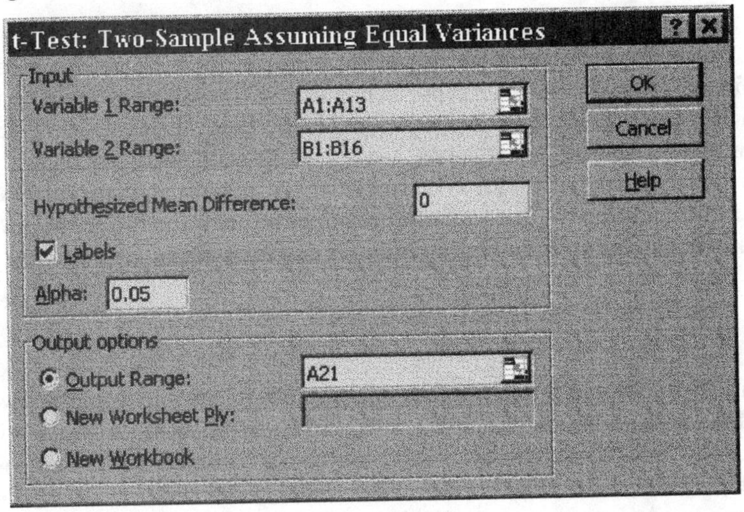

The resulting output (see Table 9.2) contains all the summary calculations necessary to easily create the desired 95% confidence interval. Notice that even the tabled t-value has been given on this printout (t Critical two tail). The construction of the confidence interval is shown below.

$$(\bar{x}_1 - \bar{x}_2) \pm t_{\alpha/2}\sqrt{s_p^2(1/n_1 + 1/n_2)}$$

Using the values found in Table 9.2, we create the following confidence interval:

$$(65.3333 - 49.4667) \pm 2.0595 \sqrt{68.016(1/12 + 1/15)}$$

$$15.8667 \pm 6.5784$$

Table 9.2

	GROUP 1	GROUP 2
Mean	65.3333333	49.46666667
Variance	43.6969697	87.12380952
Observations	12	15
Pooled Variance	68.016	
Hypothesized Mean Difference	0	
df	25	
t Stat	4.96746167	
P(T<=t) one-tail	2.0273E-05	
t Critical one-tail	1.70814019	
P(T<=t) two-tail	4.0545E-05	
t Critical two-tail	2.05953711	

Compare this value to the found in the text on page 375. This confidence interval analysis works fine whenever a small sample analysis is desired. The user must choose the appropriate relationship of the population variances, but Excel does all the work after that.

For large sample analyses, the user must be careful. We learn in the text that the individual sample variances can be used to estimate their corresponding population variances (see page 370) when constructing a large sample confidence interval to compare population means. This analysis can be done in Excel by using the t-Test: Assuming Unequal Variances analysis listed in the Data Analysis menu. The results generated by Excel, however, utilize the t distribution and should be used with caution. The statistics generated (i.e., sample means and variances) are done correctly, but the user must remember to use a z-value when creating the confidence interval. The z table shown in the text or Excels NORMSDIST function can be used to find the appropriate value to use in the confidence interval formula.

9.2.2 Tests of Hypothesis

We saw in the last section that Excel provides two methods for conducting tests to compare two independent population means. The user must decide whether the equal variance or unequal variance test is appropriate. Excel calculates both the test statistic and the p-value for the test and reports it to the user. As we have seen before in Excel, care must be taken to insure the information obtained is actually the correct information to use in making conclusions for the test. We illustrate with the following examples.

Example 9.2: We have changed Example 9.4 found on pages 374-375 of the text to conduct a test of hypothesis to compare the population means.

Behavioral researchers have developed an index designed to measure managerial success. The index (measured on a 100-point scale) is based on the manager's length of time in the organization and his or her level within the firm; the higher the index, the more successful the manager. Suppose a researcher wants to compare the average success index for two groups of managers at a large manufacturing plant. Managers in group 1 engage in a high volume of interactions with people outside the manager's work unit. (Such interactions include phone and face-to-face meetings with customers and suppliers, outside meetings, and public relations work.) Managers in group 2 rarely interact with people outside their work unit. Independent random samples of 12 and 15 managers are selected from groups 1 and 2, respectively, and the success index of each recorded. The results of the study are given in Table 9.3. Conduct a test to determine if a difference exists between the average success indexes of the managers in the two groups. Use $\alpha = .05$.

Table 9.3

GROUP 1			GROUP 2		
65	78	68	62	53	68
66	53	63	42	36	56
58	60	69	52	46	48
70	71	63	53	43	50
			57	34	42

The first step is to **Open** data file CX09_004 or **Import** the ASCII data file CXA09_04.prn. From the main menu, we next click the **Tools** menu located at the top of the Excel worksheet. Select the **Data Analysis** option from within the tools menu (see Figure 9.3). It is here the user must make a decision. There are two test of hypothesis analyses that Excel allows the user to conduct. The user must know whether an equal or unequal variance analysis is appropriate. We refer you to the text for more information on this subject. For the purpose of this example, we believe the equal variance analysis is appropriate. We next highlight the **t-Test: Two-Sample Assuming Equal Variances** option from the Analysis Tools given in the Data Analysis menu. Click **OK**.

Figure 9.3

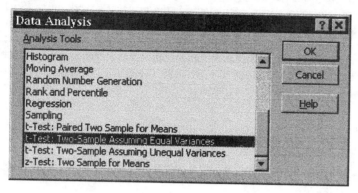

The user should now be at the t-Test menu for comparing population means (assuming equal population variances). As with all data analysis menus, the first step is to input the range of the data that is to be analyzed. Because this is a two sample problem, Excel specifies two separate locations for the input data (see Figure 9.4). Either **type** the location of the first sample or **click and drag** it's location for the Variable 1 Range and do the same for the second sample for the Variable 2 Range to input the data that you wish to compare. Enter a value of **0** for the Hypothesized Mean Difference and specify **.05** for the level of Alpha. Specify the appropriate location of the generated output by **checking** either the Output Range, New Worksheet Ply, or New Workbook option in the Output options section of the menu. Click **OK**.

Figure 9.4

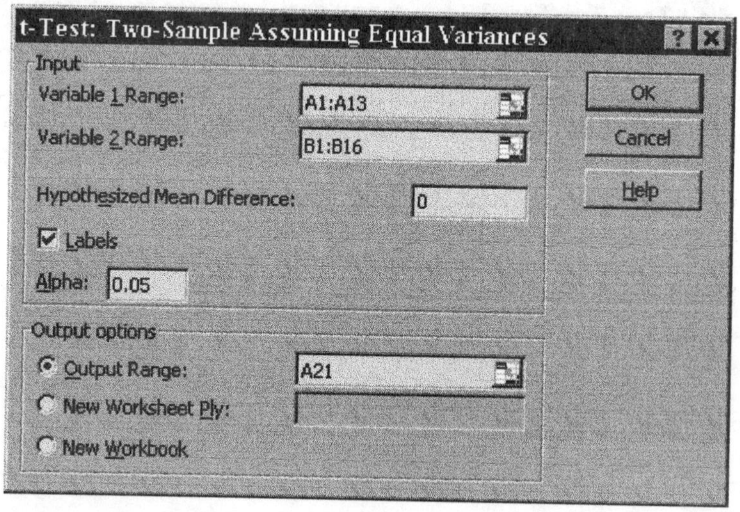

The resulting output (see Table 9.4) contains the requested test of hypothesis information. The user can either use the p-value or rejection region approach to make the appropriate conclusion for this test of hypothesis. We recommend using the p-value approach as all needed information appears on the Excel printout for small sample tests. In this example, the two-tailed p-value is given as p=0.0000405. At α=.05, there is sufficient evidence to reject H_o and conclude a difference exists between the average success indexes of managers in the two groups specified above.

Table 9.4

	GROUP 1	GROUP 2
Mean	65.3333333	49.46666667
Variance	43.6969697	87.12380952
Observations	12	15
Pooled Variance	68.016	
Hypothesized Mean Difference	0	
df	25	
t Stat	4.96746167	
P(T<=t) one-tail	2.0273E-05	
t Critical one-tail	1.70814019	
P(T<=t) two-tail	4.0545E-05	
t Critical two-tail	2.05953711	

For large sample tests, the user must be careful when working in Excel. As we discussed in the last section, the user must always specify the unequal variance t-test from Excel when using large samples. In addition, the user must be careful when using the p-values given by Excel to make conclusions for the tests of hypothesis. These p-values will be mistakenly found using the t distribution instead of the z distribution. We recommend that the user utilize the rejection region approach when making conclusions for the large sample tests of hypothesis. If the p-value approach is used, the NORMSDIST function should be used to calculate the appropriate p-value for the test of hypothesis desired. We demonstrate with the following Example.

Example 9.3: We combine the information from Examples 9.1, 9.2, and 9.3 in *Statistics for Business and Economics* below.

In recent years, the United States and Japan have engaged in intense negotiations regarding restrictions on trade between the two countries. One of the claims repeatedly by U.S. officials is that many Japanese manufacturers price their goods higher in Japan than in the United States, in effect subsidizing low prices in the United States by extremely high prices in Japan. According to the U.S. argument, Japan accomplishes this by keeping competitive U.S. goods from reaching the Japanese marketplace.

An economist decided to test the hypothesis that higher retail prices are being charged for Japanese automobiles in Japan than in the United States. She obtained random samples of 50 retail sales in the United States and 30 retail sales in Japan over the same time period and for the same model of automobile, converted the Japanese sale prices from yen to dollars using current conversion rates and obtained the summary information contained in Table 9.5. Find a p-value for the test of hypothesis when testing to determine if the mean retail price in the U.S. is less than the mean retail price in Japan.

Table 9.5

	U.S. Sales	Japan Sales
Sample Size	50	30
Sample Mean	$14,545	$15,243
Sample Std. Deviation	$ 1,989	$ 1,843

Example 9.2 on page 370 of the text calculated the test statistic of this large sample test of hypothesis to be $z = -1.59$.

We now need to calculate the observed significance level for this large sample, lower-tail test of hypothesis. Excel provides the NORMSDIST statistical function as a means to finding the desired p-value for this problem.

Open any Excel worksheet and **click** on any cell within the worksheet. Click on the function icon, f_x, at the top of the Excel worksheet. Highlight the **Statistical** function from the list of function categories available on the Paste Function menu (see Figure 9.5). Scroll down the Function name list and highlight the **NORMSDIST** function from the choices provided. Click **OK**.

Figure 9.5

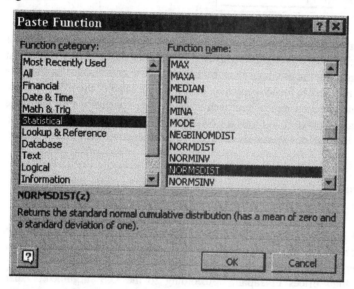

The NORMSDIST function requires the user to input information in the following format:

NORMSDIST(z)

where   **z** is the value of the test statistic calculated for the test of hypothesis to be conducted.

To find the p-value in this example, we need to enter the value of the test statistic, **z = -1.59**, into the NORMDIST Function (see Figure 9.6). Click **OK**.

Figure 9.6

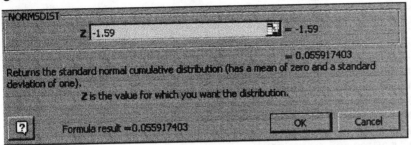

NORMDIST returns the formula result = 0.05592. This value represents the cumulative probability value of the standard normal distribution. Since we are conducting a lower tail test, this value also represents the p-value desired for this test of hypothesis problem. Compare this p-value to the one calculated in Example 9.3 *Statistics for Business and Economics* found on page 371 of the text.

The NORMSDIST function always returns the cumulative probability associated with the value of z that has been entered. The user must take care to ensure that the cumulative probability returned by Excel is, in fact, the desired p-value for the test being conducted. The cumulative probability will be correct if a lower tail test of hypothesis is desired, as was the case in the last example. If an upper tail test is conducted, subtract the cumulative probability derived from 1 to arrive at the desired p-value for the test. If a two-tailed test is desired, use a negative sign in front of the test statistic (even if a positive test statistic has been calculated) entered in the NORMSDIST function and double the cumulative probability derived to get the desired p-value. In short, the user needs to make sure that the p-value desired is found in the appropriate manner when using the NORMSDIST function within Excel.

9.3 Comparing Population Means - Paired Difference Experiments

9.3.1 Confidence Intervals

Data that has been collected from a paired difference experiment cannot be analyzed with the independent sampling analyses presented in the last section. While Excel does not provide any specific data analysis tool for working with paired data, the user can create a column of differences from the data collected and conduct a descriptive analysis on the column of differences. The output generated from this analysis can be used in both the formation of a confidence interval and in the calculation of a test statistic. We demonstrate with the example below:

Example 9.4: We use Example 9.5 found on pages 391-392 from the *Statistics for Business and Economics* text.

An experiment is conducted to compare the starting salaries of male and female college graduates who find jobs. Pairs are formed by choosing a male and a female with the same major and similar grade point averages (GPAs). Suppose a random sample of 10 pairs is formed in this manner and the starting annual salary of each person is recorded. The results are shown in Table 9.6. Compare the mean starting salary, μ_1, for males to the mean starting salary, μ_2, for females using a 95% confidence interval. Interpret the results.

Table 9.6

Pair	Male	Female	Difference
1	$29,300.00	$28,800.00	$ 500.00
2	$31,500.00	$31,600.00	$ (100.00)
3	$30,400.00	$29,800.00	$ 600.00
4	$28,500.00	$28,500.00	$ -
5	$33,500.00	$32,600.00	$ 900.00
6	$27,800.00	$28,000.00	$ (200.00)
7	$29,500.00	$29,200.00	$ 300.00
8	$31,200.00	$30,100.00	$1,100.00
9	$28,400.00	$28,200.00	$ 200.00
10	$29,200.00	$28,500.00	$ 700.00

Solution:

The first step to analyzing any paired difference experiment in Excel is to make certain that a column of differences has been computed. In this example we **Open** the Excel97 file CX09_005 (or **Import** the ASCII file CXA09_05.prn). Next, we select the **Tools** menu located at the top of the Excel worksheet. Choose the **Data Analysis** option from those listed in the Tools menu. Highlight the **Descriptive Statistics** option (see Figure 9.7) from those presented in the Data Analysis menu and click **OK**.

Figure 9.7

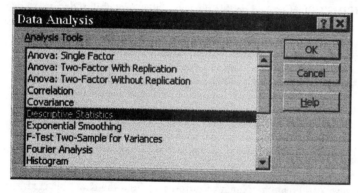

The column of differences in the data should be typed (**D1:D11**, in this example) into the Input Range of the Descriptive Statistics menu (see Figure 9.8). The Output Range should be specified (**D13**, in this example), and the Summary Statistics and Confidence Level for Mean boxes both **checked**. In addition, the level of confidence desired should be entered (**95**, in this example) in the appropriate space. Click **OK**.

Figure 9.8

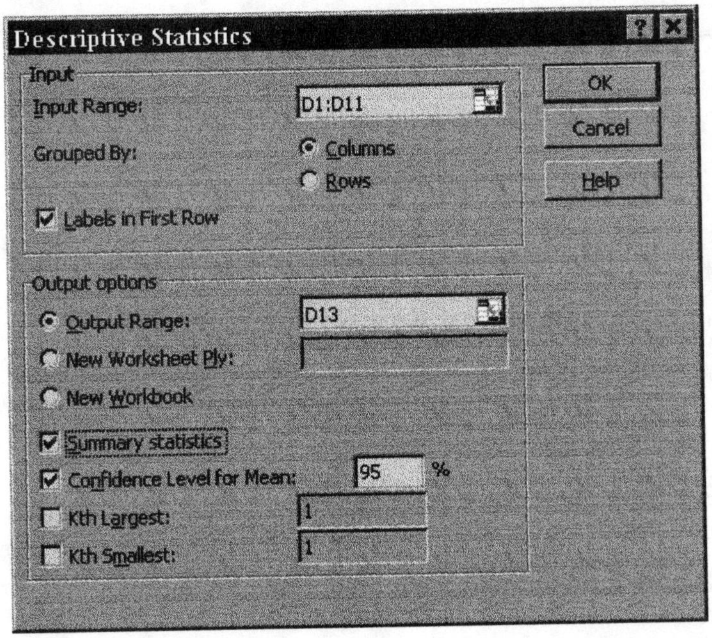

The output generated from this menu is shown in Table 9.7. The usual summary statistics are shown as well as the 95% confidence level value. As we saw in Chapter 7, this value should be added and subtracted from the value of the sample mean to calculate the upper and lower endpoints of the confidence interval. In this example, the endpoints of the interval are found in the following manner:

Mean $\pm$ Confidence Level(95%) value

400 ± 310.904

The 95% confidence intervals goes from 89.096 to 710.904. Compare these values to the ones found on page 392 of the text.

For large sample analyses, the user must be careful. The confidence values generated by Excel utilize the t distribution and should not be used when a large sample has been collected. The statistics generated by Excel (i.e., sample means and variances) can be used, but the user must remember to use a z-value when creating the large sample confidence interval. The z table shown in the text or Excel's NORMSDIST function can be used to find the appropriate value to use in the confidence interval formula.

Table 9.7

Difference	
Mean	400
Standard Error	137.4368542
Median	400
Mode	#N/A
Standard Deviation	434.6134937
Sample Variance	188888.8889
Kurtosis	-1.086183885
Skewness	0.152265108
Range	1300
Minimum	-200
Maximum	1100
Sum	4000
Count	10
Confidence Level(95.0%)	310.9040011

9.4 Comparing Two Population Variances

Excel gives us an easy method of testing to determine the relationship between two population variances. The procedure is very similar to the two sample test of hypothesis used when comparing two population means. We illustrate this method with the example below.

Example 9.5: We use Example 9.13 found on pages 414-415 in the *Statistics for Business and Economics* text.

In Examples 9.1 and 9.2 (Example 9.4 in the text), we used the two-sample t statistic to compare the success indexes of the two groups of managers. The data are repeated in Table 9.8 for convenience. The use of the t statistic was based on the assumption that the population variances of the managerial success indexes were equal for the two groups. Use the computer to check this assumption at $\alpha = .10$.

Table 9.8

GROUP 1			GROUP 2		
65	78	68	62	53	68
66	53	63	42	36	56
58	60	69	52	46	48
70	71	63	53	43	50
			57	34	42

Solution:

The first step is to **Open** data file CX09_013 or **Import** the ASCII data file CXA09_13.prn. From the main menu, we next click the **Tools** menu located at the top of the Excel worksheet. Select the **Data Analysis** option from within the tools menu (see Figure 9.9). We next highlight the **F-Test Two Sample for Variances** option from the Analysis Tools given in the Data Analysis menu. Click **OK**.

Figure 9.9

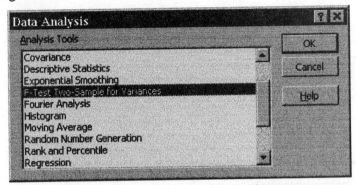

The user should now be at the F-Test menu for comparing population variances. As with all data analysis menus, the first step is to input the range of the data that is to be analyzed. Because this is a two sample problem, Excel specifies two separate locations for the input data (see Figure 9.10). Either **type** the location of the first sample or **click and drag** it's location for the Variable 1 Range and do the same for the second sample for the Variable 2 Range to input the data that you wish to compare. Enter a value of **0** for the Hypothesized Mean Difference and specify **.10** for the level of Alpha. Specify the appropriate location of the generated output by **checking** either the Output Range, New Worksheet Ply, or New Workbook option in the Output options section of the menu. Click **OK**.

Figure 9.10

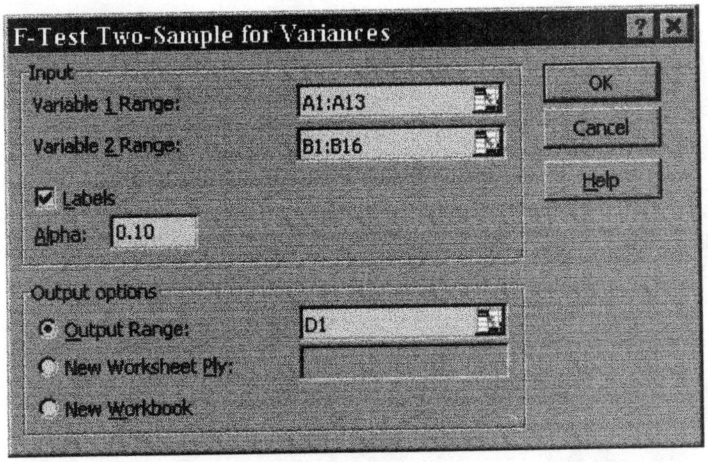

The resulting output (see Table 9.9) contains the requested test of hypothesis information. The user can either use the p-value or rejection region approach to make the appropriate conclusion for this test of hypothesis. We recommend using the p-value approach as all needed information appears on the Excel printout for small sample tests. In this example, the one-tailed p-value is given as p=0.12769. The two-tailed p-value would be 0.12769 x 2 = 0.25538.   Compare this value to the p-value found on page 415 of the text. For α=.10, there is insufficient evidence to reject H_o. Therefore, we cannot conclude that a difference exists between the variances of the success indexes of managers in the two groups specified above.

Table 9.9

	Group 1	Group 2
Mean	65.33333333	49.46666667
Variance	43.6969697	87.12380952
Observations	12	15
df	11	14
F	0.501550264	
P(F<=f) one-tail	0.127690676	
F Critical one-tail	0.458879157	

Chapter 10
Simple Linear Regression

10.1 Introduction

Chapters 10-12 in *Statistics for Business and Economics* introduce the topic of regression analysis to the reader. Chapter 10 serves as the introduction of the general concepts of simple linear regression. Simple linear regression is how the text introduces the theories and concepts of mathematical modeling to the reader. These topics are then expanded in Chapters 11 and 12 of the text.

We will take a similar approach to regression as does the text. We will use Chapter 10 to introduce you to the methods Excel offers to work with regression analysis. We will see how Excel can be used to calculate both the correlation and the linear modeling ideas that are presented in the text. We will use the chapter examples that are given in the text to illustrate these methods. The following examples from *Statistics for Business and Economics* are solved with Microsoft Excel® in this chapter:

Excel Companion		Statistics for Business and Economics	
Example	Page	SBE Example	SBE Page
10.1	111	10.1	463
10.2	114	10.2	466

10.2 The Coefficient of Correlation

Regression analysis is all about the relationship between variables. Chapters 10-12 spend time developing the mathematical modeling of one variable using the values of other related variables. The simplest form of this modeling idea is the linear relationship between two variables. This idea, known as correlation, is studied in Chapter 10 of *Statistics for Business and Economics*. We examine how Excel calculates correlations below.

Example 10.1: Use Example 10.1 found on page 463 of *Statistics for Business and Economics* text.

Legalized gambling is available on several riverboat casinos operated by a city in Mississippi. The mayor of the city wants to know the correlation between the number of casino employees and the yearly crime rate. The records for the past 10 years are examined and the results listed in Table 10.1 are obtained. Calculate the coefficient of correlation r for the data.

Table 10.1

Year	Number of Employees	Crime Rate
1987	15	1.35
1988	18	1.63
1989	24	2.33
1990	22	2.41
1991	25	2.63
1992	29	2.93
1993	30	3.41
1994	32	3.26
1995	35	3.63
1996	38	4.15

Solution:

The first step is to **Open** data file CX10_001 or **Import** the ASCII data file CXA10_01.prn. From the main menu, we next click the **Tools** menu located at the top of the Excel worksheet. Select the **Data Analysis** option from within the tools menu. We next highlight the **Correlation** option (see Figure 10.1) from the Analysis Tools given in the Data Analysis menu. Click **OK**.

Figure 10.1

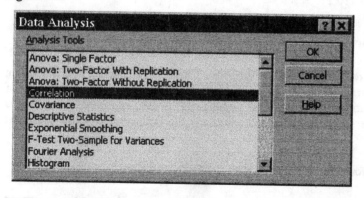

You should now be in the Correlation menu (see Figure 10.2). Enter the location of the two variables that you wish to correlate. Either **click on the cells** or **type** this location in the Input Range location in the Correlation menu. Specify where the output is desired and either **check** the Output Range, New Worksheet Ply, or New Workbook. Specify the appropriate name or location of your output selection. Click **OK**.

Figure 10.2

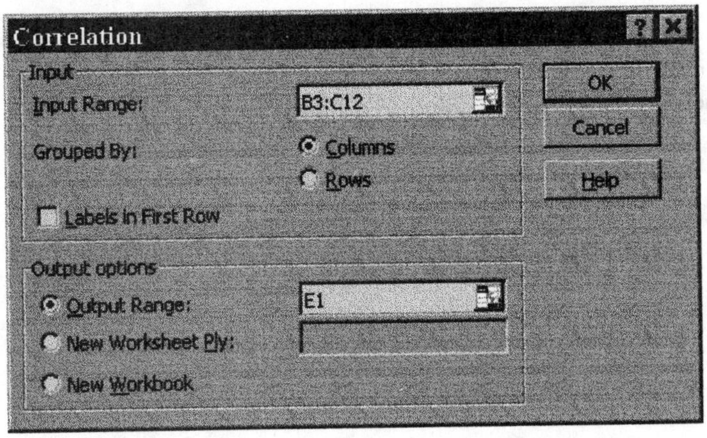

The correlation output is a table of the two variables that were specified in the Input Range of the Correlation menu above. The numbers presented in this table represent the coefficients of correlation of the variables selected. The correlation that is desired is the one that is located in the Column 1 column and the Column 2 row. The value in this example is 0.98703 (see Table 10.2). Compare this value to the one found in the text on page 463.

Table 10.2

	Column 1	Column 2
Column 1	1	
Column 2	0.98703	1

10.3 The Coefficient of Determination and Regression Output

After studying the topic of correlation, the next step in learning regression analysis is understanding the modeling concepts. Our goal in regression is to build a mathematical relationship that attempts to predict the value of one variable, y, with the values of other related variables, the x's. Chapter 10 presents the simplest form of this modeling idea -- simple linear regression. In it, a single independent variable, x, is hypothesized to have a straight-line relationship with the dependent variable, y.

The example that we use from *Statistics for Business and Economics* asks the reader to calculate the coefficient of determination from the data. Our purpose here is to use the data from the example to generate the basic simple linear regression output with Excel. As you will see, the coefficient of determination is one of the components of this output.

Example 10.2: We use Example 10.2 found on pages 466-467 of the *Statistics for Business and Economics* text.

Calculate the coefficient of determination for the advertising-sales example that is used as an example throughout the text. The data are shown below in Table 10.3 for convenience.

Table 10.3

Advertising Expenditures, x (100s)	Sales Revenue, y ($1,000s)
1	1
2	1
3	2
4	2
5	4

Solution:

The first step is to **Open** data file CX10_002 or **Import** the ASCII data file CXA10_02.prn. From the main menu, we next click the **Tools** menu located at the top of the Excel worksheet. Select the **Data Analysis** option from within the tools menu. We next highlight the **Regression** option (see Figure 10.3) from the Analysis Tools given in the Data Analysis menu. Click **OK**.

Figure 10.3

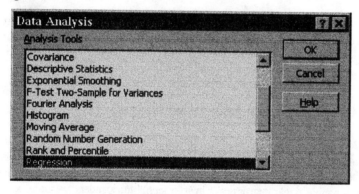

You should now be in the Regression menu (see Figure 10.4). Enter the location of the dependent variable, y, that you wish to use in the regression equation. Either **click on the cells** or **type** this location in the Input Y Range location in the Input area of the Regression menu. **Repeat** this procedure for your independent variable, x. Specify where the output is desired and either **check** the Output Range, New Worksheet Ply, or New Workbook. Specify the appropriate name or location of your output selection. Click **OK**. [Note: None of the optional boxes need to be checked here in the regression menu. We will explore these options in Chapters 11 and 12 of the text]

Figure 10.4

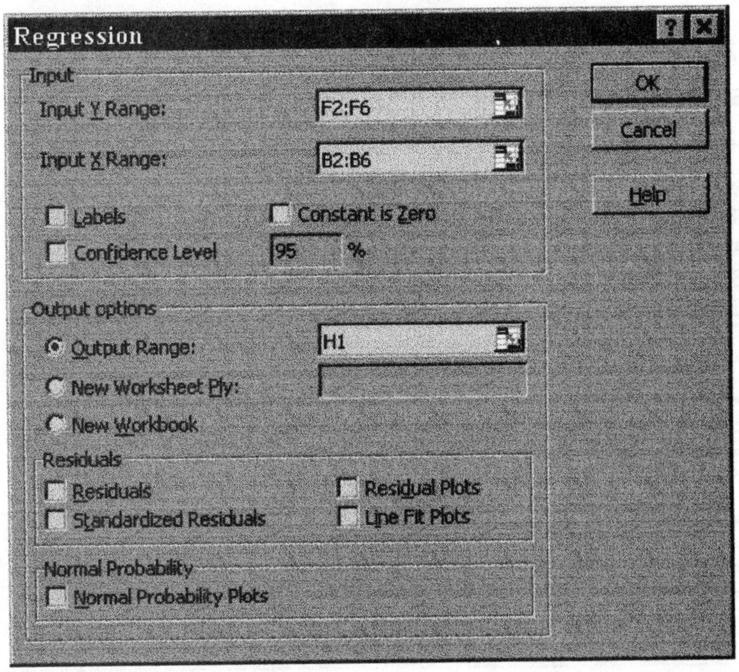

The results of the regression menu selections are shown in Table 10.4. In addition to the desired coefficient of determination, the simple linear regression model is given. We point out the most important features of the printout generated by Excel. Compare these values to those shown on indicated pages of the text.

Excel Printout Values	Description of Values
Multiple R = 0.903696	Coefficient of correlation (page 463)
R Square = 0.816667	Coefficient of determination (page 467)
Standard Error = 0.605530	Square Root of MSE or s (page 447)
Intercept Coefficient = -0.1	Estimate of β_0 (page 438)
X Variable 1 Coefficient = 0.7	Estimate of β_1 (page 438)
T Stat for X Variable 1 = 3.655631	Test statistic for testing β_1 (page 452)
P-value for X Variable 1 = 0.03535	P-value for testing β_1 (page 452)

We find the value of the coefficient of determination is found on the Excel printout to be $R^2 = 0.816667$. Many of the other values presented in Table 10.4 will be discussed in Chapters 11 and 12. As we stated earlier in this chapter, our goal in Chapter 10 is to provide the Excel procedures that will generate the basic regression outputs. We will add to this work in the next two chapters.

Table 10.4

SUMMARY OUTPUT

Regression Statistics	
Multiple R	0.903696114
R Square	0.816666667
Adjusted R Square	0.755555556
Standard Error	0.605530071
Observations	5

ANOVA

	df	SS	MS	F	Significance F
Regression	1	4.9	4.9	13.36364	0.035352847
Residual	3	1.1	0.366667		
Total	4	6			

	Coefficients	Std. Error	t Stat	P-value	Lower 95%	Upper 95%	Lower 95.0%	Upper 95.0%
Intercept	-0.1	0.635085	-0.15746	0.884884	-2.12112675	1.92112675	-2.12112675	1.92112675
X Variable 1	0.7	0.191485	3.655631	0.035353	0.090607356	1.309392644	0.090607356	1.309392644

Chapter 11
Multiple Regression

11.1 Introduction

Chapters 11 in *Statistics for Business and Economics* introduces the topic of **multiple** regression analysis to the reader. While Chapter 10 served as the introduction to the general concepts of simple linear regression, Chapter 11 expands these concepts to modeling with several variables. In addition, Chapter 11 examines some of the problems associated with regression analysis and gives methods of detecting and solving these problems.

We utilize Chapter 11 examples to build on the linear regression base developed in the preceding chapter. Through the use of the Regression data analysis tool, Excel allows the user to build more sophisticated models than the linear models of Chapter 10. We examine both the model building methods and the residual analysis options offered within Excel. We will use the chapter examples that are given in the text to illustrate these methods. The following examples from *Statistics for Business and Economics* are solved with Microsoft Excel® in this chapter:

Excel Companion		Statistics for Business and Economics	
Example	Page	SBE Example	SBE Page
11.1	117	11.1	510
11.2	120	11.2	520
11.3	123	11.3	521
11.4	127	11.5	546

11.2 Multiple Regression Model Building

We have seen in Chapter 10 how to use Excel to build a simple linear regression model using one independent variable, x. The next step in our regression process is to add more independent variables into the regression model. Excel allows for this using the same menus as seen in the simple linear regression chapter. We use an example from the text below.

Example 11.1: We use Example 11.1 found on pages 510 - 511 in the *Statistics for Business and Economics* text.

A collector of antique grandfather clocks know that the price received for the clocks increases linearly with the age of the clocks. Moreover, the collector hypothesizes that the auction price of the clocks will increase linearly as the number of bidders increase. Thus, the following model is hypothesized:

$$y = \beta_0 + \beta_1 x_1 + \beta_2 x_2 + \varepsilon$$

A sample of 32 auction prices of grandfather clocks, along with their age and the number of bidders is shown in Table 11.1. The model $y = \beta_0 + \beta_1 x_1 + \beta_2 x_2 + \varepsilon$ is fit to the data. Use Excel to:

a.   Test the hypothesis that the mean auction price of a clock increases as the number of bidders increases when age is held constant, that is, $\beta_2 > 0$. Use $\alpha = .05$.

b.   Interpret the estimates of the β coefficients in the model.

Table 11.1

Age (x_1)	Number of Bidders (x_2)	Auction Price (y)	Age (x_1)	Number of Bidders (x_2)	Auction Price (y)
127	13	$ 1,235	170	14	2,131
115	12	1,080	182	8	1,550
127	7	845	162	11	1,884
150	9	1,522	184	10	2,041
156	6	1,047	143	6	845
182	11	1,979	159	9	1,483
156	12	1,822	108	14	1,055
132	10	1,253	175	8	1,545
137	9	1,297	108	6	729
113	9	946	179	9	1,792
137	15	1,713	111	15	1,175
117	11	1,024	187	8	1,593
137	8	1,147	111	7	785
153	6	1,092	115	7	744
117	13	1,152	194	5	1,356
126	10	1,336	168	7	1,262

Solution:

We need to generate the multiple regression model hypothesized above using Excel. The printout generated must include the individual coefficient estimates and the corresponding t-tests of those parameters. Fortunately, the standard Excel regression output yields both of the desired values.

We begin by **opening** Excel97 file CX11_001 (or **importing** CXA11_01.prn). At the main menu, click on the **Tools** menu located at the top of the Excel worksheet. Select the **Data Analysis** option from within the Tools menu and highlight the **Regression** option from the choices given in the Data Analysis menu (see Figure 11.1). Click **OK**.

Figure 11.1

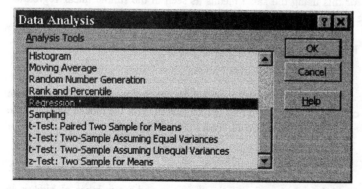

Inside the Regression menu, enter the dependent variable (Auction Price) into the Input Y Range by either typing or **clicking on the cells** where the dependent variable is located (see Figure 11.2). **Repeat** this procedure for the independent variables (Age and Number of Bidders). The only other item that needs to be entered is the choice for where the output will be generated at in the Output Options section of the Regression menu. **Check** either the Output Range, New Worksheet Ply, or New Workbook and **specify** the location or name in the space provided in the menu. Click **OK**. We will examine the other options in this menu in subsequent examples in this chapter.

Figure 11.2

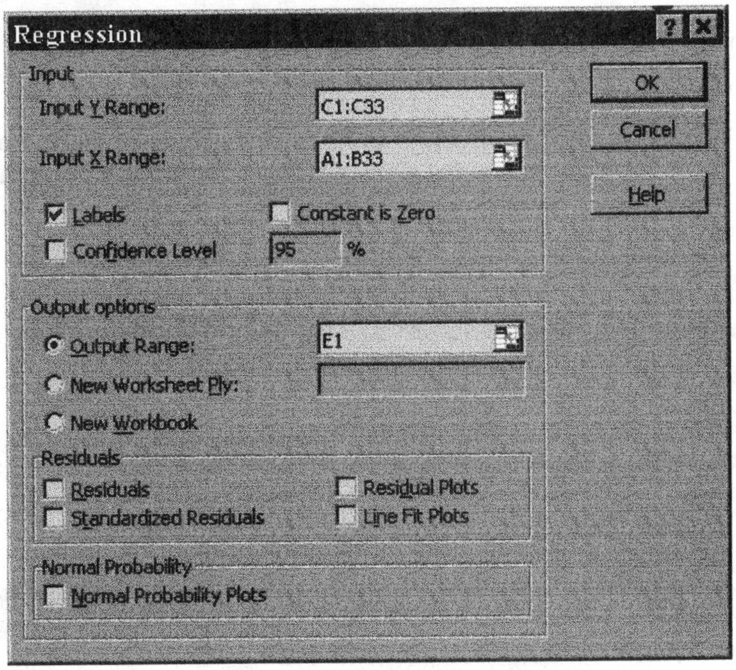

Excel generates the output shown in Table 11.2 below.

Table 11.2

SUMMARY OUTPUT

Regression Statistics	
Multiple R	0.94463957
R Square	0.89234392
Adjusted R Square	0.88491936
Standard Error	133.484668
Observations	32

ANOVA

	df	SS	MS	F	Sign. F
Regression	2	4283062.96	2141531.48	120.1881617	9.21636E-15
Residual	29	516726.54	17818.1565		
Total	31	4799789.5			

	Coefficients	Standard Error	t Stat	P-value	Lower 95%	Upper 95%	Lower 95.0%	Upper 95.0%
Intercept	-1338.95134	173.8094707	-7.703558	1.706E-08	-1694.4318	-983.47087	-1694.43182	-983.470865
Age (x1)	12.7405741	0.904740307	14.082023	1.693E-14	10.8901714	14.5909768	10.89017139	14.5909768
Number of Bidders (x2)	85.9529844	8.728523289	9.8473684	9.345E-11	68.1011401	103.804829	68.10114007	103.8048287

Compare this output to the MINITAB output shown on page 511 of the text. In order to test whether the price of a clock increase as the number of bidders increases, holding age constant, we use the test statistic and p-value shown on the printout for the x_2 variable. The printout shows that $t = 9.847$ and $p \approx 0$. The estimates of the β coefficients can be found in the Coefficients column in the printout. Our estimate of β_0, β_1, and β_2 are -1338.95, 12.74, and 85.95, respectively. We refer you to the text for more detailed information regarding the interpretations and conclusions that should be made for these values.

The next step of a regression analysis is to test all the hypothesized variables simultaneously. We refer to this process as checking the usefulness of the model. This process is illustrated in the following example.

Example 11.2: We use Example 11.2 found on pages 520 - 521 in the *Statistics for Business and Economics* text.

A collector of antique grandfather clocks know that the price received for the clocks increases linearly with the age of the clocks. Moreover, the collector hypothesizes that the auction price of the clocks will increase linearly as the number of bidders increase. Thus, the following model is hypothesized:

$$y = \beta_0 + \beta_1 x_1 + \beta_2 x_2 + \varepsilon$$

A sample of 32 auction prices of grandfather clocks, along with their age and the number of bidders is shown in Table 11.3. The model $y = \beta_0 + \beta_1 x_1 + \beta_2 x_2 + \varepsilon$ is fit to the data. Use Excel to:

a.   Find and interpret the coefficient of determination R^2 for this example.
b.   Conduct the global F-test of model usefulness at the $\alpha = .05$ level of significance.

Solution:

We need to generate the multiple regression model hypothesized above using Excel. The printout generated must include the coefficient of determination and the F-test statistic and/or p-value. As we saw in the last example, the standard Excel regression output yields both of the desired values.

We begin by **opening** Excel97 file CX11_002 (or **importing** CXA11_02.prn). At the main menu, click on the **Tools** menu located at the top of the Excel worksheet. Select the **Data Analysis** option from within the Tools menu and highlight the **Regression** option from the choices given in the Data Analysis menu (see Figure 11.3). Click **OK**.

Table 11.3

Age (x₁)	Number of Bidders (x₂)	Auction Price (y)	Age (x₁)	Number of Bidders (x₂)	Auction Price (y)
127	13	$ 1,235	170	14	2,131
115	12	1,080	182	8	1,550
127	7	845	162	11	1,884
150	9	1,522	184	10	2,041
156	6	1,047	143	6	845
182	11	1,979	159	9	1,483
156	12	1,822	108	14	1,055
132	10	1,253	175	8	1,545
137	9	1,297	108	6	729
113	9	946	179	9	1,792
137	15	1,713	111	15	1,175
117	11	1,024	187	8	1,593
137	8	1,147	111	7	785
153	6	1,092	115	7	744
117	13	1,152	194	5	1,356
126	10	1,336	168	7	1,262

Figure 11.3

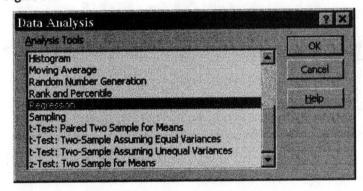

Inside the Regression menu, enter the dependent variable (Auction Price) into the Input Y Range by either **typing** or **clicking on the cells** where the dependent variable is located (see Figure 11.4). **Repeat** this procedure for the independent variables (Age and Number of Bidders). The only other item that needs to be entered is the choice for where the output will be generated at in the Output Options section of the Regression menu. **Check** either the Output Range, New Worksheet Ply, or New Workbook and **specify** the location or name in the space provided in the menu. Click **OK**. We will examine the other options in this menu in subsequent examples in this chapter.

Figure 11.4

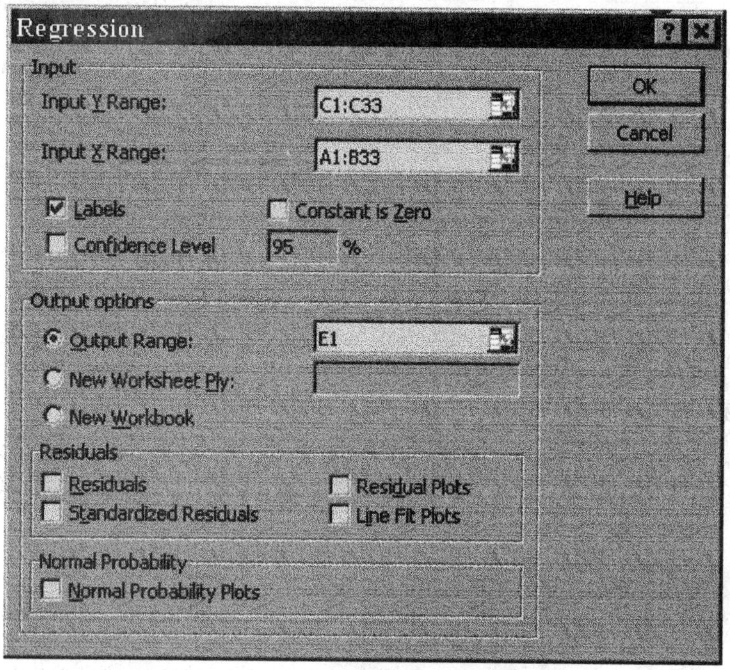

Excel generates the output shown in Table 11.4 below.

Table 11.4

SUMMARY OUTPUT

Regression Statistics	
Multiple R	0.94463957
R Square	0.89234392
Adjusted R Square	0.88491936
Standard Error	133.484668
Observations	32

ANOVA

	df	SS	MS	F	Sign. F
Regression	2	4283062.96	2141531.48	120.1881617	9.21636E-15
Residual	29	516726.54	17818.1565		
Total	31	4799789.5			

	Coefficients	Standard Error	t Stat	P-value	Lower 95%	Upper 95%	Lower 95.0%	Upper 95.0%
Intercept	-1338.95134	173.8094707	-7.703558	1.706E-08	-1694.4318	-983.47087	-1694.43182	-983.470865
Age (x1)	12.7405741	0.904740307	14.082023	1.693E-14	10.8901714	14.5909768	10.89017139	14.5909768
Number of Bidders (x2)	85.9529844	8.728523289	9.8473684	9.345E-11	68.1011401	103.804829	68.10114007	103.8048287

The coefficient of determination, R^2, is listed as the R Square value in the Regression Statistics table above. The R^2 value of $R^2 = 0.8923$ can be compare to the value shown on page 520 of the text. The global F statistic and p-value are both shown in the ANOVA table in the printout above. The global F statistic of $F = 120.188$ and the p-value of $p \approx 0$ are identical to the values shown in the text on page 520. We refer you to the text for more detailed information regarding the interpretations and conclusions that should be made for these values.

We have seen how Excel can be used to model several independent variables. We now add the interaction component between two variables to the regression model. Excel treats this as though another independent variable has been entered into the regression model. The products of these interactions ($x_1 * x_2$) should appear in a column of data adjacent to the other independent variables to be entered into the regression equation. We demonstrate with the following example.

Example 11.3: We use Example 11.2 found on pages 521 - 522 of the *Statistics for Business and Economics* text.

A collector of antique grandfather clocks know that the price received for the clocks increases linearly with the age of the clocks. Moreover, the collector hypothesizes that the auction price of the clocks will increase linearly as the number of bidders increase. Thus, the following model is hypothesized:

$$y = \beta_0 + \beta_1 x_1 + \beta_2 x_2 + \varepsilon$$

Suppose the collector, having observed many auctions, believes that the *rate of increase* of the auction price with age will be driven upward by the large number of bidders. The collector proposes the following interaction model:

$$y = \beta_0 + \beta_1 x_1 + \beta_2 x_2 + \beta_3 x_1 x_2 + \varepsilon$$

A sample of 32 auction prices of grandfather clocks, along with their age and the number of bidders is shown in Table 11.5. The model $y = \beta_0 + \beta_1 x_1 + \beta_2 x_2 + \beta_3 x_1 x_2 + \varepsilon$ is fit to the data. Use Excel to test the hypothesis that the price-age slope increases as the number of bidders increases -- that is, that age and number of bidders, x_2, interact positively.

Table 11.5

Age (x_1)	Number of Bidders (x_2)	Auction Price (y)	Age (x_1)	Number of Bidders (x_2)	Auction Price (y)
127	13	$ 1,235	170	14	2,131
115	12	1,080	182	8	1,550
127	7	845	162	11	1,884
150	9	1,522	184	10	2,041
156	6	1,047	143	6	845
182	11	1,979	159	9	1,483
156	12	1,822	108	14	1,055
132	10	1,253	175	8	1,545
137	9	1,297	108	6	729
113	9	946	179	9	1,792
137	15	1,713	111	15	1,175
117	11	1,024	187	8	1,593
137	8	1,147	111	7	785
153	6	1,092	115	7	744
117	13	1,152	194	5	1,356
126	10	1,336	168	7	1,262

Solution:

We need to generate the interaction model hypothesized above using Excel. The printout generated must include the t-test statistic and/or p-value for the interaction test. If we treat the $x_1 x_2$ interaction term as a new independent variable, Excel allows the desired information to be obtained.

We begin by **opening** Excel97 file CX11_003 (or **importing** CXA11_03.prn). At the main menu, click on the **Tools** menu located at the top of the Excel worksheet. Select the **Data Analysis** option from within the Tools menu and highlight the **Regression** option from the choices given in the Data Analysis menu (see Figure 11.5). Click **OK**.

Figure 11.5

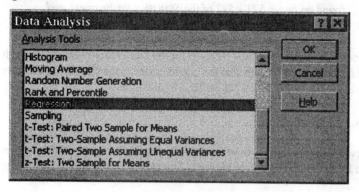

Inside the Regression menu, enter the dependent variable (y) into the Input Y Range by either **typing** or **clicking on the cells** where the dependent variable is located (see Figure 11.6). **Repeat** this procedure for the independent variables (x_1, x_2, and the interaction term x_1x_2). The only other item that needs to be entered is the choice for where the output will be generated at in the Output Options section of the Regression menu. **Check** either the Output Range, New Worksheet Ply, or New Workbook and **specify** the location or name in the space provided in the menu. Click **OK**. We will examine the other options in this menu in subsequent examples in this chapter.

The printouts generated are shown in Table 11.6. To determine if age and the number of bidders interact positively, we use the t statistic and p-value shown for the Age*Number of Bidder row of the printout. The value of the test statistic, t = 6.112, and the value of the p-value, p =.00000135, can be compared to the values in the MINITAB printout shown on page 522 of the *Statistics for Business and Economics* text. We refer you to the text for more detailed information regarding the interpretations and conclusions that should be made for these values.

Figure 11.6

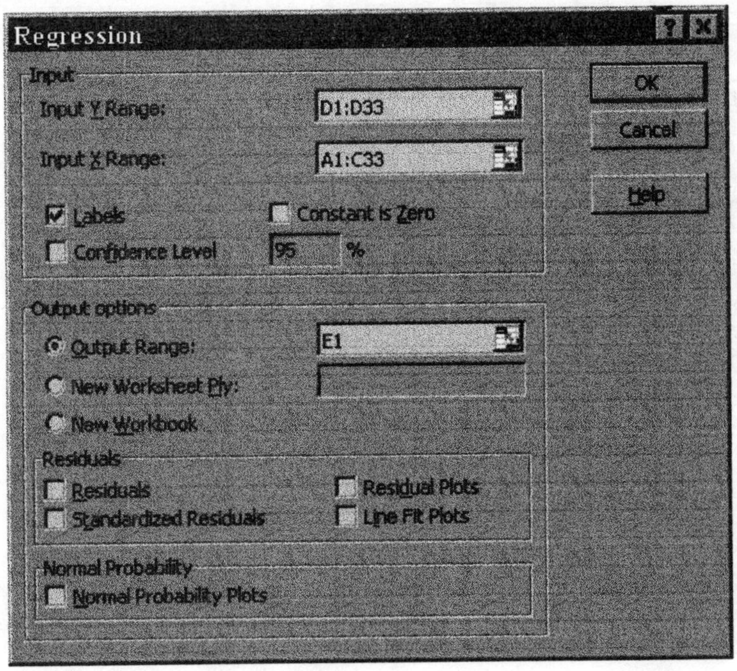

Table 11.6

SUMMARY OUTPUT

Regression Statistics	
Multiple R	0.976668248
R Square	0.953880866
Adjusted R Square	0.948939531
Standard Error	88.91451215
Observations	32

ANOVA

	df	SS	MS	F	Significance F
Regression	3	4578427.37	1526142.46	193.0410958	8.34956E-19
Residual	28	221362.133	7905.79047		
Total	31	4799789.5			

	Coefficients	Standard Error	t Stat	P-value	Lower 95%	Upper 95%	Lower 95.0%	Upper 95.0%
Intercept	320.4579934	295.141285	1.0857783	0.286837	-284.1122	925.028188	-284.112202	925.0281882
Age (x1)	0.878142475	2.03215593	0.4321236	0.668961	-3.2845449	5.04082987	-3.28454492	5.04082987
Number of Bidders (x2)	-93.26482436	29.89161615	-3.1200998	0.004165	-154.49509	-32.034556	-154.495093	-32.0345556
Age*Number of Bidders (x1*x2)	1.297845824	0.212332598	6.1123249	1.35E-06	0.86290172	1.73278992	0.862901724	1.732789923

11.3 Residual Analysis in Excel

In the last section, we examined how to build multiple regression models in Excel. We will see more variations of model building in Chapter 12. We now turn our attention to the residual analysis topic that is covered in Section 11.8 of the text. Through the many options available in the Regression analysis tool, Excel provides many of the plots and analyses that are necessary to conduct a residual analysis of the proposed regression model. The Regression analysis tool menu is shown below in Figure 11.7.

Figure 11.7

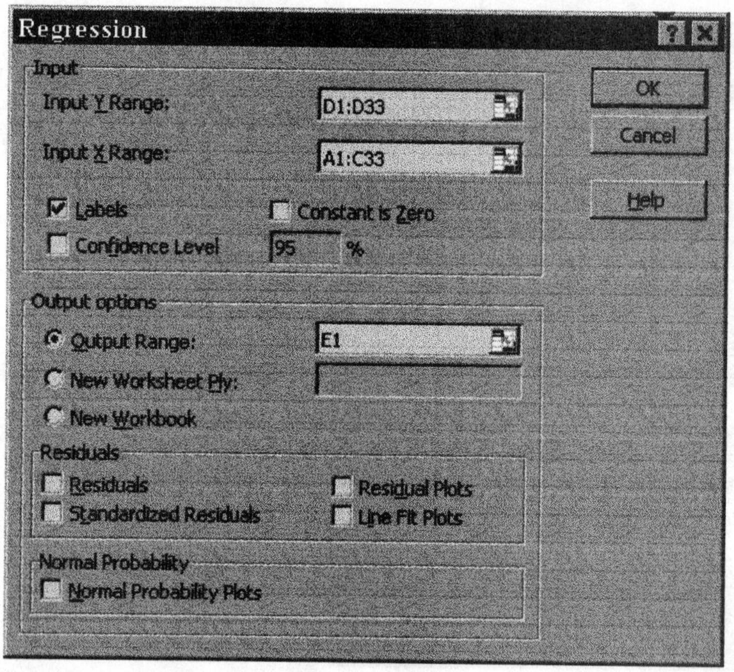

Before demonstrating the various options, we list the options available as well as a brief discussion regarding their use in a residual analysis of a regression model.

Residuals   Provides a listing of the residuals for the hypothesized regression model.

Standardized   Provides a listing of the standardized residuals for the hypothesized regression model.
Residuals

Residual   Generates a scatter plot for the regression residuals plotted against each of the independent
Plots   variables entered into the regression model.

Line Fit   Generates a scatter plot for each independent variable of both the predicted and the
Plots   observed values plotted against the values of the independent variable.

Normal Prob. Generates a normal probability plot for the regression residuals
Plot

The listed output and plots can be used to interpret the results of a residual analysis of the regression model proposed. We refer you to Section 11.8 of *Statistics for Business and Economics* for a thorough discussion of these and other related residual analysis topics. We demonstrate using Excel in a residual analysis with the following example.

Example 11.4: We use Example 11.5 and 11.6 found on pages 546 -549 of the *Statistics for Business and Economics* text.

The data for the grandfather clock example used throughout this chapter are repeated in Table 11.7, with one important difference: The auction price of the clock at the top of the second column has been changed from $2,131 to $1,131. The interaction model

$$y = \beta_0 + \beta_1x_1 + \beta_2x_2 + \beta_3x_1x_2 + \varepsilon$$

is again fit to these (modified) data. Use Excel to generate all corresponding residual analysis printouts.

Table 11.7

AGE X1	NUMBER OF BIDDERS X2	AUCTION PRICE Y	AGE X1	NUMBER OF BIDDERS X2	AUCTION PRICE Y
127	13	1235	170	14	1131
115	12	1080	182	8	1550
127	7	845	162	11	1884
150	9	1522	184	10	2041
156	6	1047	143	6	845
182	11	1979	159	9	1483
156	12	1822	108	14	1055
132	10	1253	175	8	1545
137	9	1297	108	6	729
113	9	946	179	9	1792
137	15	1713	111	15	1175
117	11	1024	187	8	1593
137	8	1147	111	7	785
153	6	1092	115	7	744
117	13	1152	194	5	1356
126	10	1336	168	7	1262

Solution:

The first step in this solution is to fit the proposed regression model to the modified grandfather clock data. We will follow closely the Excel instructions used in Example 11.3 and change only the requested residual analysis and normal probability output.

We begin by **opening** Excel97 file CX11_005 (or **importing** CXA11_05.prn). At the main menu, click on the **Tools** menu located at the top of the Excel worksheet. Select the **Data Analysis** option from within the Tools menu and highlight the **Regression** option from the choices given in the Data Analysis menu (see Figure 11.8). Click **OK**.

Figure 11.8

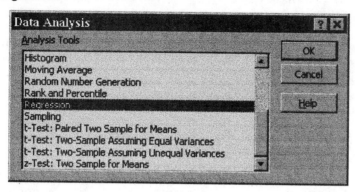

Inside the Regression menu, enter the dependent variable (y) into the Input Y Range by either **typing or clicking on the cells** where the dependent variable is located (see Figure 11.9). **Repeat** this procedure for the independent variables (x_1, x_2, and the interaction term x_1x_2). **Check** either the Output Range, New Worksheet Ply, or New Workbook and **specify** the location or name in the space provided in the menu. To request the residual plots and the normal probability plot, check the boxes corresponding to the **Residuals, Standardized Residuals, Residual Plots, Line Fit Plots,** and **Normal Probability Plots**. Click **OK**.

Figure 11.9

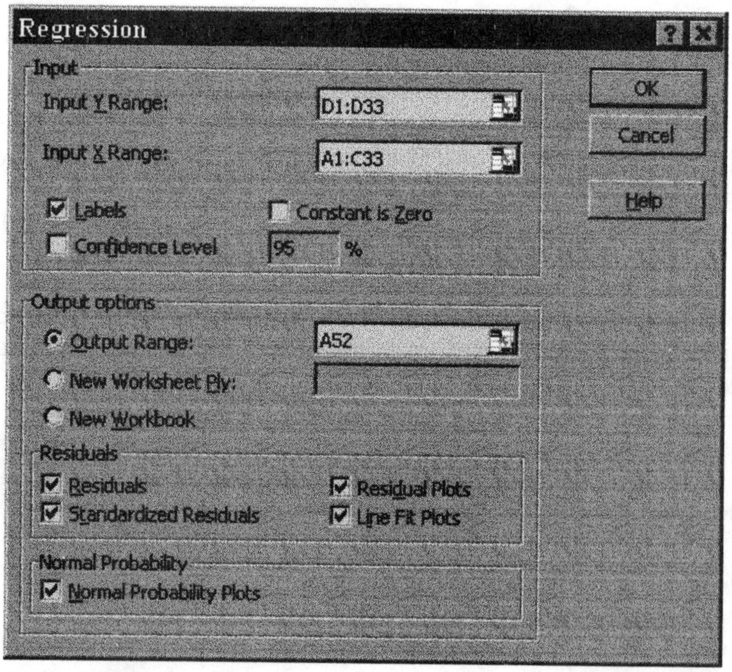

Our purpose in this section is to illustrate the different types of Excel output that are available and to give the commands necessary to generate these output. We will refer you to Section 11.8 of the text for information regarding the assessment and interpretation of these printouts. We point out here the various output generated by the different options within Excel.

We begin with the standard regression output generated by Excel (see Table 11.9). This output includes the summary output table, the ANOVA table for the proposed regression model, and the individual coefficient estimates along with their corresponding confidence and test of hypothesis information. This output is provided whenever a regression model is specified in the Regression menu of Excel. No residual or normal probability option need to be specified in order to generate this standard regression output.

Table 11.9

SUMMARY OUTPUT

Regression Statistics	
Multiple R	0.85391853
R Square	0.72917685
Adjusted R Square	0.70016009
Standard Error	200.597562
Observations	32

ANOVA

	df	SS	MS	F	Sign. F
Regression	3	3033586.804	1011196	25.1295	4.2774E-08
Residual	28	1126702.696	40239.38		
Total	31	4160289.5			

	Coefficients	Standard Error	t Stat	P-value	Lower 95%	Upper 95%	Lower 95.0%	Upper 95.0%
Intercept	-512.81017	665.8600588	-0.77015	0.447662	-1876.7642	851.143862	-1876.7642	851.1438618
AGE X1	8.16507852	4.584690573	1.780944	0.085775	-1.2262449	17.556402	-1.22624494	17.55640198
BIDDERS X2	19.8876621	67.4376453	0.294904	0.770242	-118.25225	158.027572	-118.252247	158.0275715
AGE*BID, X1*X2	0.31964386	0.47903768	0.667262	0.510067	-0.6616214	1.30090916	-0.66162145	1.300909165

The Residuals and Standardized Residuals options ask Excel to compute these values and display them in tabular form. Table 11.10 provides the requested information for this example. We refer the reader to Section 11.8 of *Statistics for Business and Economics* for more details regarding how this table can be used in the residual analysis portion of a regression analysis.

Table 11.10

Observation	Predicted AUCTION PRICE Y	Residuals	Standardized Residuals
1	1310.42642	-75.42641826	-0.395639519
2	1105.93433	-25.93432854	-0.136035165
3	947.531826	-102.531826	-0.537817429
4	1322.45977	199.5402255	1.046662438
5	1179.4547	-132.4547022	-0.694774005
6	1831.92541	147.0745936	0.771460754
7	1597.96733	224.0326744	1.17513441
8	1185.78671	67.2132924	0.35255863
9	1178.91542	118.0845776	0.619397375
10	913.910465	32.08953518	0.168321505
11	1560.98865	152.0113539	0.797355891
12	1072.64994	-48.64994469	-0.255186991
13	1115.23655	31.76344818	0.166611058
14	1149.20588	-57.20587718	-0.300066028
15	1187.22193	-35.22193162	-0.184752086
16	1117.61761	218.382395	1.145496601
17	1914.43283	-783.4328287	-4.109395551
18	1597.73687	-47.73687377	-0.250397596
19	1598.30219	285.6978126	1.498590915
20	1776.5856	264.4144036	1.386951547
21	1048.37646	-203.3764606	-1.066784913
22	1421.83663	61.16336641	0.320824526
23	1130.74709	-75.74709239	-0.397321574
24	1522.68127	22.31873186	0.117070021
25	695.473502	33.52649759	0.175858906
26	1642.6741	149.3259017	0.783269699
27	1224.0355	-49.03550027	-0.257209373
28	1651.34802	-58.34802065	-0.306056994
29	781.090458	3.909542288	0.020506998
30	822.7008	-78.70079979	-0.412814864
31	1480.70791	-124.7079148	-0.654139234
32	1374.03783	-112.0378323	-0.587679955

The Residual Plots option in the Regression menu of Excel plots the residuals calculated by Excel versus the independent variables that were hypothesized in the regression model. Figure 11.10 shows the residuals plotted against independent variables x_1 and x_2. We note here that a residual plot versus the interaction term x_1x_2 is also generated by Excel but not reproduced here. Please refer to Section 11.8 of *Statistics for Business and Economics* for more details regarding how these plots can be used in the residual analysis portion of a regression analysis.

Figure 11.10

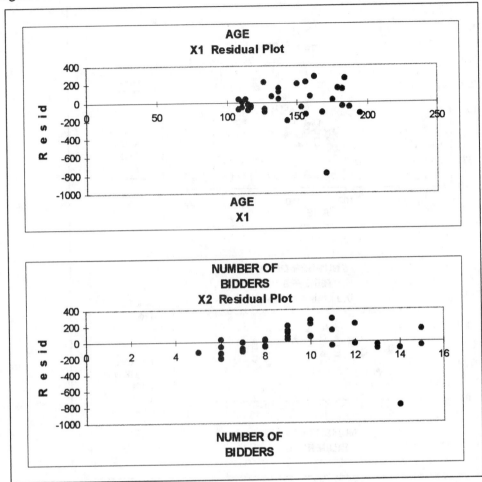

The Line Fits Plot option generates a plot that compares the observed and predicted y-values of the analysis to each of the independent variables entered in the proposed regression model. Figure 11.11 gives the plots for the independent variables x_1 and x_2 for the current example. We note here that a line fit plot for the interaction term x_1x_2 is also generated by Excel but not reproduced here. While not extremely useful plots in this example due to the interaction component in the model, these plots can aid in assessing the usefulness of the regression model. Please refer to Section 11.8 of *Statistics for Business and Economics* for more details regarding how these plots can be used in the residual analysis portion of a regression analysis.

Figure 11.11

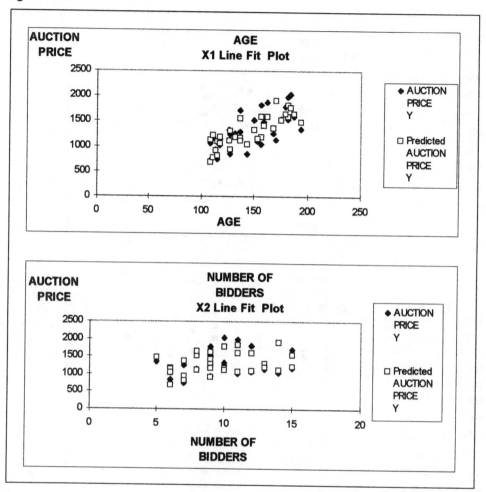

The Normal Probability Plot option generates a plot that can be used to assess the distribution of the random error component of the proposed regression model. Figure 11.12 gives the normal probability plot that results from fitting the interaction model to the data of this example. The straighter the line on the normal probability plot, the more closely the distribution of the random error component resembles a normal distribution.

Figure 11.12

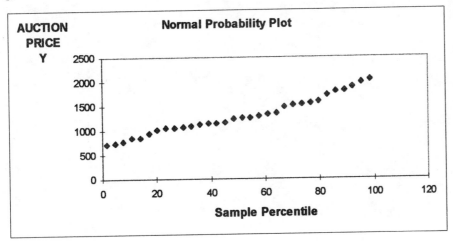

Compare the output and plots generated in Excel to those found on pages 547 - 549 of the *Statistics for Business and Economics* text. The Excel analyses compare favorably with those generated with other statistical software packages.

Included in the data set disk is Example 11.4 (Excel file CX11_004) from the *Statistics for Business and Economics* text. It follows the same regression menu as the last example and generates the corresponding residual analysis output and plots. We leave it to the user to practice with Excel on this data set. Compare the results generated with those found on pages 543 - 545 of the text.

Chapter 12
Model Building

12.1 Introduction

Chapter 12 is the last of the three regression chapters in the *Statistics for Business and Economics* text. It expands the multiple regression material presented in Chapter 11 to include more independent variable options for modeling the dependent variable. It begins by introducing the two types of independent variables: quantitative and qualitative variables. Chapter 12 then uses these two types of variables to demonstrate the modeling concept of regression analysis. Through the use of chapter examples, models with increasing complexity are fit and the regression results analyzed. Chapter 12 also discusses the Partial F test for comparing regression models and the Stepwise Regression model building method.

As we have seen in Chapter 11, Excel allows a variety of variables to be used as independent variables in a regression analysis. The Regression data analysis tool within Excel will again be used to build the regression models of Chapter 12. In addition, Excel can also be used to conduct the Partial F test that is shown in Section 12.5 of the text. The method we will use involves fitting two different regression models and comparing the outputs produced. The Stepwise procedure shown in Section 12.9 of the *Statistics for Business and Economics* text cannot be conducted in Excel at the present time.

We will use the chapter examples that are given in the text to illustrate the model building and testing methods discussed above. The following examples from *Statistics for Business and Economics* are solved with Microsoft Excel® in this chapter:

Excel Companion		Statistics for Business and Economics	
Example	**Page**	**SBE Example**	**SBE Page**
12.1	136	12.2	583
12.2	139	12.5	612
12.3	142	12.7	622

12.2 Models With Quantitative Variables

We have seen the model building concept presented in Chapter 11. The main idea involves identifying variables that you suspect do a good job of predicting, or modeling, the value of the dependent variable. Chapter 12 introduces the reader to the two main types of independent variables; quantitative and qualitative. We begin by demonstrating the modeling of quantitative independent variables. We will then look at modeling qualitative variables and finish with regression models that incorporate both quantitative and qualitative variables. We start with an example from the text.

Example 12.1: We use Example 12.2 found on pages 583 - 585 in the *Statistics for Business and Economics* text.

Power companies have to be able to predict the peak power load at their various stations in order to operate efficiently. The peak power load is the maximum amount of power that must be generated each day in order to meet demand.

Suppose a power company in the southern part of the United States decides to model daily peak power load, y, as a function of the daily high temperature, x, and the model is to be constructed for the summer months when the demand is greatest. Although we would expect the peak power load to increase as the high temperature increases, the *rate* of increase in $E(y)$ might also increase as x increases. That is, a 1-unit increase in high temperature from 100 to 101° F might result in a larger increase in power demand than would a 1-unit increase from 80 to 81° F. Therefore, we postulate the second-order model

$$E(y) = \beta_0 + \beta_1 x + \beta_2 x^2$$

and we would expect β_2 to be positive.

A random sample of 25 summer days is selected, and the data are shown below in Table 12.1 Fit a second-order model using these data, and test the hypothesis that the power load increases at an increasing *rate* with temperature--i.e., that $\beta_2 > 0$.

Table 12.1

Temperature (°F)	Peak Load (megawatts)	Temperature (°F)	Peak Load (megawatts)
94	136	100	151.9
96	131.7	79	106.2
95	140.7	97	153.2
108	189.3	98	150.1
67	96.5	87	114.7
88	116.4	76	100.9
89	118.5	68	96.3
84	113.4	92	135.1
90	132	100	143.6
106	178.2	85	111.4
67	101.6	89	116.5
71	92.5	74	103.9
		86	105.1

Solution:

We need to generate the multiple regression model hypothesized above using Excel. The printout generated must include the individual coefficient estimates and the corresponding t-test for the quadratic term in the model. Fortunately, the standard Excel regression output yields both of the desired values.

We begin by **opening** Excel97 file CX12_002 (or **importing** CXA12_02.prn). At the main menu, click on the **Tools** menu located at the top of the Excel worksheet. Select the **Data Analysis** option from within the Tools menu and highlight the **Regression** option from the choices given in the Data Analysis menu (see Figure 12.1). Click **OK**.

Figure 12.1

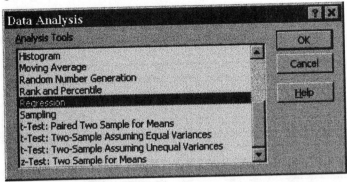

Inside the Regression menu, enter the dependent variable (Peak Load) into the Input Y Range by either **typing or clicking on the cells** where the dependent variable is located (see Figure 12.2). **Repeat** this procedure for the independent variables (Temperature and Temperature Squared). We note here that the variable columns for both Temperature and Temperature Squared must be adjacent to one another in the data set when entering these variables into the Input X range in this menu. The only other item that needs to be entered is the choice for where the output will be generated at in the Output Options section of the Regression menu. **Check** either the Output Range, New Worksheet Ply, or New Workbook and **specify** the location or name in the space provided in the menu. Click **OK**. We will examine the other options in this menu in subsequent examples in this chapter.

Figure 12.2

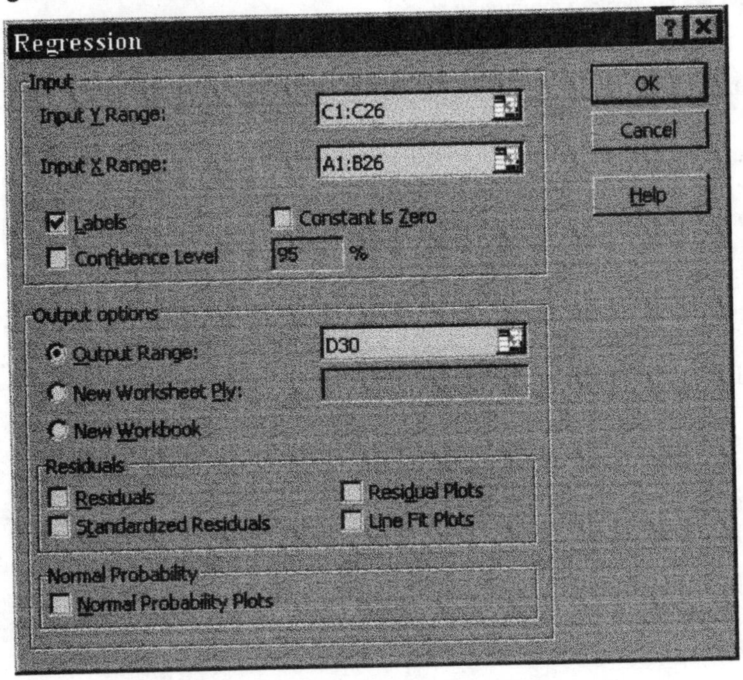

Excel generates the output shown in Table 12.2 below.

Table 12.2

SUMMARY OUTPUT

Regression Statistics	
Multiple R	0.979470618
R Square	0.959362691
Adjusted R Square	0.95566839
Standard Error	5.376203469
Observations	25

ANOVA

	df	SS	MS	F	Significance F
Regression	2	15011.772	7505.885999	259.687216	4.99085E-16
Residual	22	635.8784022	28.90356374		
Total	24	15647.6504			

	Coefficients	Standard Error	t Stat	P-value	Lower 95%	Upper 95%	Lower 95.0%	Upper 95.0%
Intercept	385.0480932	55.17243578	6.978993909	5.2661E-07	270.6273418	499.4688447	270.6273418	499.4688447
Temperature (oF)	-8.292526804	1.29904502	-6.383556132	2.00975E-06	-10.98658418	-5.598469431	-10.98658418	-5.598469431
Temperature Sqrd.	0.059823368	0.007548554	7.925142711	6.8979E-08	0.044168609	0.075478128	0.044168609	0.075478128

Compare this output to the MINITAB output shown on page 584 of the text. In order to test whether the power load increases at an increasing rate with temperature, we use the test statistic and p-value shown on the printout for the x^2 variable. The printout shows that $t = 7.925143$ and $p \approx 0$. We refer you to the text for more detailed information regarding the interpretations and conclusions that should be made for these values.

Models can be specified with any number and/or arrangement of quantitative independent variables. If other quantitative variables are to be used, both the linear and quadratic forms of these variables can be entered as in the example above. Excel also allows the interaction between variables to be used as an independent variable. The desired interaction terms must appear as a column of values adjacent to the other independent variables in the data set. Together, all columns must be entered into the Input X Range area of the regression menu to generate the desired interaction model.

12.3 Models With Qualitative Variables

Suppose we are trying to use a regression model to predict the annual salary of a manager of a particular department store. We saw in the last section how quantitative data, such as age and years of experience, can be used in a regression model. Variables such as gender, race, and job title, however, cannot be modeled in the same manner. As discussed in the text, qualitative variables rely on the use of indicator, or dummie, variables to indicate which level of the qualitative variable is correct. These indicator variables behave like a switch by either turning on or off the various levels of the qualitative variable. For example, if the goal of an analysis is to predict a specific female manager's annual salary, the indicator variable for gender would turn the female level "on" while turning the male level "off".

By defining the indicator variables correctly within a data set, Excel can be used to fit regression models with qualitative variables. We refer the reader to Section 12.6 of the *Statistics for Business and Economics* text for further discussions concerning the indicator variables. We demonstrate how to use qualitative variables within Excel in the following example.

Example 12.2: We use Example 12.5 found on pages 612 - 614 in the *Statistics for Business and Economics* text.

Suppose the manager of a department store chain wants to compare the mean dollar amounts owed by delinquent credit card customers in three different annual income groups: less than $25,000, $25,000-$60,000, and more than $60,000. A sample of 10 customers with delinquent accounts is selected from each group and shown in Table 12.3 below. Do the data provide sufficient evidence to indicate that the mean dollar amounts owed by customers differ for the three annual income groups?

Solution:

The first step necessary when solving this problem is to define the independent variables in such a manner that is useful to Excel. Refer to the text for more information regarding the use of indicator variables in regression models. Since their are three levels of the variable Income Level, we must define the following two indictor variables:

$$x_1 = \begin{cases} 1 \text{ if group 2} \\ 0 \text{ if not} \end{cases} \qquad x_2 = \begin{cases} 1 \text{ if group 3} \\ 0 \text{ if not} \end{cases}$$

The Excel data set used in the regression calculations is shown in Table 12.4.

Table 12.3

Group 1 < $25,000	Group 2 $25,000-$60,000	Group 3 >$60,000
148	513	335
76	264	643
393	433	216
520	94	536
236	535	128
134	327	723
55	214	258
166	135	380
415	280	594
153	304	465

Table 12.4

Y	X₁	X₂	Y	X₁	X₂
148	0	0	327	1	0
76	0	0	214	1	0
393	0	0	135	1	0
520	0	0	280	1	0
236	0	0	304	1	0
134	0	0	335	0	1
55	0	0	643	0	1
166	0	0	216	0	1
415	0	0	536	0	1
153	0	0	128	0	1
513	1	0	723	0	1
264	1	0	258	0	1
433	1	0	380	0	1
94	1	0	594	0	1
535	1	0	465	0	1

The Regression data analysis tool in Excel can now be used to fit the following regression model:

$$E(y) = \beta_0 + \beta_1 x + \beta_2 x_2$$

The goal is to generate the multiple regression model hypothesized above using Excel. The printout generated must include the standard regression output in order to conduct the desired global-F. Fortunately, the standard Excel regression output yields the needed information.

We begin by **opening** Excel97 file CX12_005 (or **importing** CXA12_05.prn). At the main menu, click on the **Tools** menu located at the top of the Excel worksheet. Select the **Data Analysis** option from within the Tools menu and highlight the **Regression** option from the choices given in the Data Analysis menu (see Figure 12.3). Click **OK**.

Figure 12.3

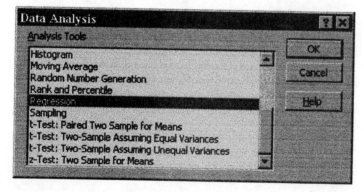

Inside the Regression menu, enter the dependent variable (Y) into the Input Y Range by either **typing** or **clicking on the cells** where the dependent variable is located (see Figure 12.4). **Repeat** this procedure for the independent variables (X₁ and X₂). We note here that the variable columns for both X₁ and X₂ must be adjacent to one another in the data set when entering these variables into the Input X range in this menu. The only other item that needs to be entered is the choice for where the output will be generated at in the Output Options section of the Regression menu. **Check** either the Output Range, New Worksheet Ply, or New Workbook and **specify** the location or name in the space provided in the menu. Click **OK**.

Figure 12.4

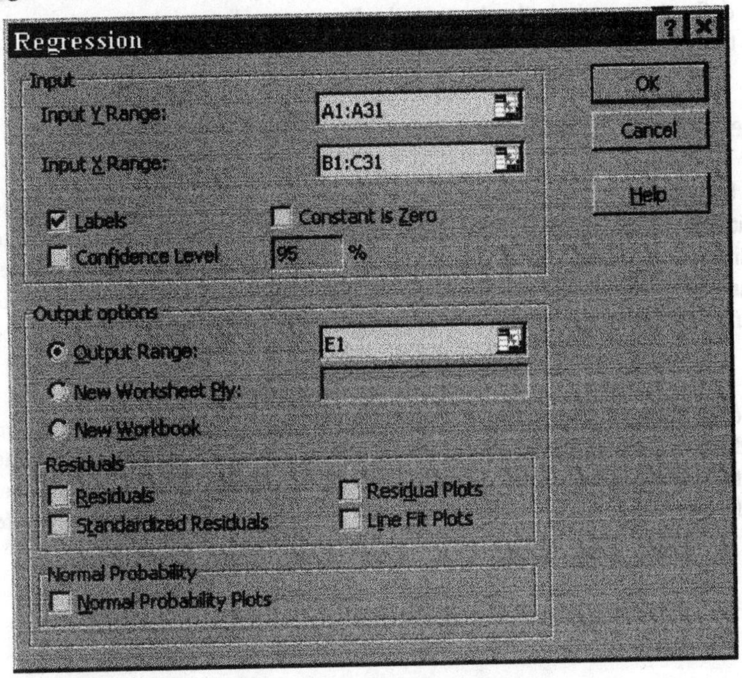

Excel generates the output shown in Table 12.5 below.

Table 12.5

SUMMARY OUTPUT

Regression Statistics	
Multiple R	0.452811
R Square	0.205038
Adjusted R Square	0.146152
Standard Error	168.9478
Observations	30

ANOVA

	df	SS	MS	F	Significance F
Regression	2	198772.467	99386.2333	3.48193801	0.045152103
Residual	27	770670.9	28543.3667		
Total	29	969443.367			

	Coefficients	Standard Error	t Stat	P-value	Lower 95%	Upper 95%	Lower 95.0%	Upper 95.0%
Intercept	229.6	53.42599243	4.2975336	0.0002	119.978992	339.221008	119.9789918	339.2210082
X1	80.3	75.55576307	1.0627912	0.29729	-74.727517	235.327517	-74.7275165	235.3275165
X2	198.2	75.55576307	2.6232281	0.01415	43.1724835	353.227517	43.17248347	353.2275165

Compare this output to the SAS output shown on page 614 of the text. In order to determine whether the mean dollar amounts owed by customers differ for the three annual income groups, we use the test statistic and p-value shown on the printout for the global-F test. The printout shows that F = 3.4819 and p = 0.0451. We refer you to the text for more detailed information regarding the interpretations and conclusions that should be made for these values.

Excel can be used to accommodate any number of qualitative variables with any numbers of levels. Once the indicator variables have been defined correctly in the data set, the Regression data analysis tools can be utilized. We next look at models that contain both quantitative and qualitative variables.

12.4 Comparing Two Regression Models

We have seen how Excel can be used to fit regression models with just quantitative variables and regression models with just qualitative variables. For more complicated models, Excel allows the user to input both quantitative and qualitative variables into a single multiple regression model. The variables must be located in adjacent columns of data within the Excel worksheet. By specifying the appropriate columns in the Regression data analysis menu, any number of quantitative and qualitative variables can be combined.

The final step in the model building topic is to develop a method that allows the user to compare two regression models to determine which is the better predictor of the dependent variable. Section 12.5 in the text details the partial-F test for testing a portion of the regression model. By fitting two separate model within Excel, it is possible to calculate the partial-F test statistic that the book details. We demonstrate with the following example.

Example 12.3: We use Example 12.7 found on pages 622 - 625 in the *Statistics for Business and Economics* text.

An industrial psychologist conducted an experiment to investigate the relationship between worker productivity and a measure of salary incentive for two manufacturing plants; one, plant A, had union representation and the other, plant B, had nonunion representation. The productivity y per worker was measured by recording the number of machined castings that a worker could produce in a four-week period of 40 hours per week. The incentive was the amount x_1 of bonus (in cents per casting) paid for all castings produced in excess of 1,000 per worker for the four-week period. Nine workers were selected from each plant, and three from each group of nine were assigned to receive a 20¢ bonus per casting, three a 30¢ bonus, and three a 40¢ bonus. The productivity data for the nine workers, three for each plant type and incentive combination, are shown in Table 12.6.

a. Assume that the relationship between mean productivity and incentive is first-order. Plot the data points and graph the prediction equations for the two productivity lines.

b. Do the data provide sufficient evidence to indicate a difference in mean worker responses to incentives between the two plants?

Table 12.6

TYPE OF PLANT	INCENTIVE		
	$.20/casting	$.30/casting	$.40/casting
Union Plant	1,435	1,583	1,601
	1,512	1,529	1,574
	1,491	1,610	1,636
Non-Union Plant	1,575	1,635	1,645
	1,512	1,589	1,616
	1,488	1,661	1,689

Solution:

The first step necessary when solving this problem is to define the independent variables in such a manner that is useful to Excel. Refer to the text for more information regarding the use of indicator variables in regression models. The Incentive variable can be modeled with a single quantitative variable, x_1 but the Plant variable must use an indicator variable. Since their are two levels of the Plant variable, we must define the following indictor variable, x_2:

$$x_1 = \text{Incentive} \qquad x_2 = \begin{cases} 1 \text{ if nonunion plant} \\ 0 \text{ if union plant} \end{cases}$$

We start by building a regression model that allows for interaction between our two independent variables, $E(y) = \beta_0 + \beta_1 x + \beta_2 x_2 + \beta_3 x_1 x_2$. Since it is desired to determine if there is a difference in mean worker responses to incentives between the two plants, our goal is to test Ho: $\beta_2 = \beta_3 = 0$. We will need to fit two regression models in order to conduct the desired partial-F test:

Complete Model: $E(y) = \beta_0 + \beta_1 x + \beta_2 x_2 + \beta_3 x_1 x_2$
Reduced Model: $E(y) = \beta_0 + \beta_1 x$

The Excel data set used to fit both of these regression models is shown in Table 12.7.

Table 12.7

INCENTIVE X1	PLANT TYPE X2	X1*X2	PRODUCTION Y
0.2	0	0	1435
0.2	0	0	1512
0.2	0	0	1491
0.2	1	0.2	1575
0.2	1	0.2	1512
0.2	1	0.2	1488
0.3	0	0	1583
0.3	0	0	1529
0.3	0	0	1610
0.3	1	0.3	1635
0.3	1	0.3	1589
0.3	1	0.3	1661
0.4	0	0	1601
0.4	0	0	1574
0.4	0	0	1636
0.4	1	0.4	1645
0.4	1	0.4	1616
0.4	1	0.4	1689

We build the complete model above by using the Regression data analysis tool in Excel. We begin by **opening** Excel97 file CX12_007 (or **importing** CXA12_07.prn). At the main menu, click on the **Tools** menu located at the top of the Excel worksheet. Select the **Data Analysis** option from within the Tools menu and highlight the **Regression** option from the choices given in the Data Analysis menu (see Figure 12.5). Click **OK**.

Figure 12.5

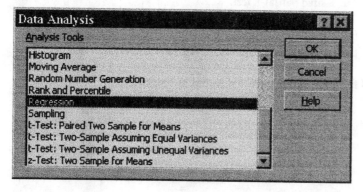

Inside the Regression menu, enter the dependent variable (Y) into the Input Y Range by either **typing or clicking on the cells** where the dependent variable is located (see Figure 12.6). **Repeat** this procedure for the independent variables (X_1, X_2, and X_1X_2). We note here that the variable columns for both X_1, X_2, and X_1X_2 must be adjacent to one another in the data set when entering these variables into the Input X range in this menu. The only other item that needs to be entered is the choice for where the output will be generated at in the Output Options section of the Regression menu. **Check** either the Output Range, New Worksheet Ply, or New Workbook and **specify** the location or name in the space provided in the menu. Click **OK**.

Figure 12.6

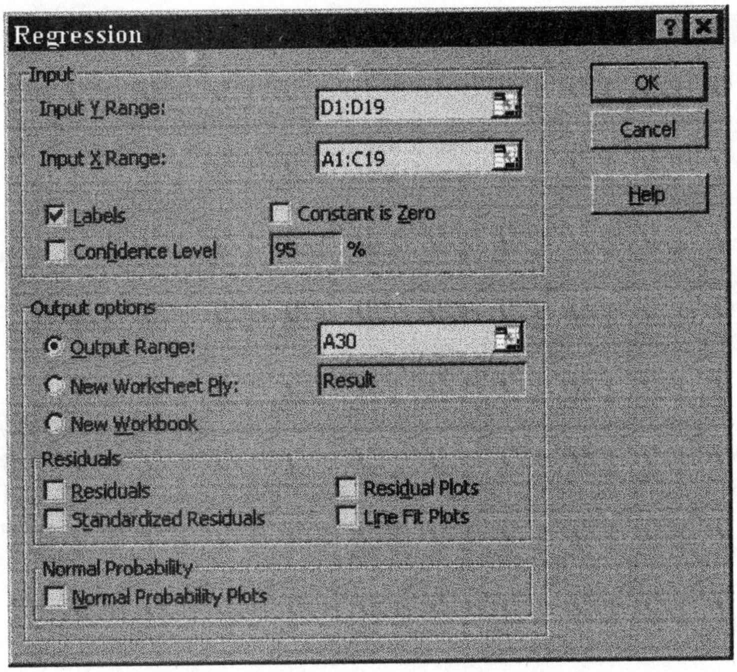

Excel generates the output shown in Table 12.8 below.

Table 12.8

SUMMARY OUTPUT - COMPLETE MODEL

Regression Statistics	
Multiple R	0.8429712
R Square	0.71060045
Adjusted R Square	0.64858626
Standard Error	40.8387266
Observations	18

ANOVA

	df	SS	MS	F	Significance F
Regres	3	57332.3889	19110.7963	11.45867497	0.000461532
Residu	14	23349.2222	1667.80159		
Total	17	80681.6111			

	Coefficients	Standard Error	t Stat	P-value	Lower 95%	Upper 95%	Lower 95.0%	Upper 95.0%
Intercept	1365.83333	51.83641257	26.35	2.5E-13	1254.65519	1477.01148	1254.655187	1477.01148
INCENTIVE X1	621.666667	166.723403	3.729	0.00225	264.080213	979.25312	264.0802132	979.2531201
PLANT TYPE X2	47.7777778	73.30775769	0.652	0.52512	-109.45186	205.00742	-109.451865	205.0074204
X1 * X2	3.33333333	235.7824977	0.014	0.98892	-502.37028	509.036946	-502.370279	509.0369455

We notice that the $SSE_c = 23,349.22$ and the $MSE_c = 1,667.80$. Compare these values to the ones found in the MINITAB printout on page 623 of the text.

This process must be repeated for the reduced model in order to compare the regression outputs for the two models. At the main menu, click on the **Tools** menu located at the top of the Excel worksheet. Select the

Data Analysis option from within the Tools menu and highlight the **Regression** option from the choices given in the Data Analysis menu (see Figure 12.7). Click **OK**.

Figure 12.7

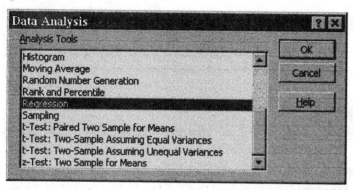

Inside the Regression menu, enter the dependent variable (Y) into the Input Y Range by either **typing** or **clicking on the cells** where the dependent variable is located (see Figure 12.8). **Repeat** this procedure for the independent variable (X_1). The only other item that needs to be entered is the choice for where the output will be generated at in the Output Options section of the Regression menu. **Check** either the Output Range, New Worksheet Ply, or New Workbook and **specify** the location or name in the space provided in the menu. Click **OK**.

Figure 12.8

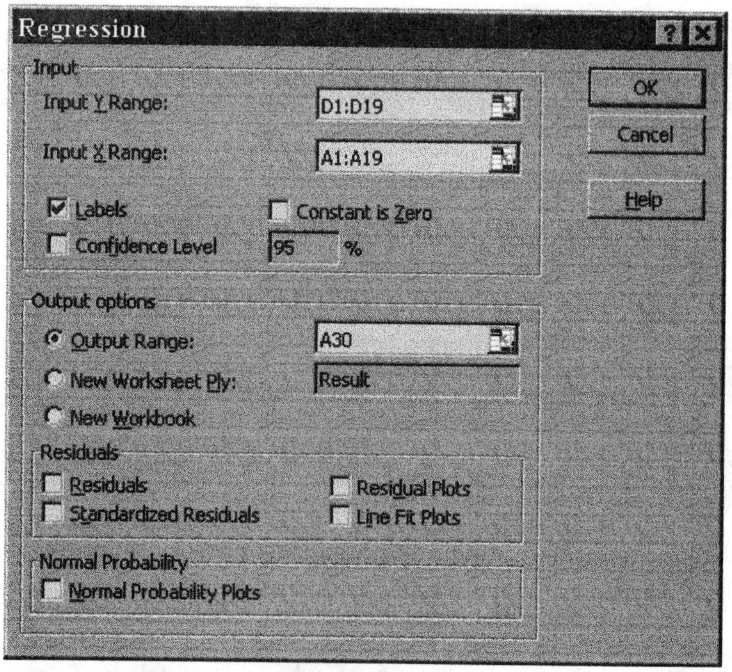

Excel generates the output shown in Table 12.9 below.

Table 12.9

```
SUMMARY OUTPUT - REDUCED MODEL
```

Regression Statistics	
Multiple R	0.7601927
R Square	0.57789294
Adjusted R Square	0.55151125
Standard Error	46.1358577
Observations	18

ANOVA

	df	SS	MS	F	Significance F
Regression	1	46625.3333	46625.3333	21.90507542	0.000250782
Residual	16	34056.2778	2128.51736		
Total	17	80681.6111			

	Coefficients	Standard Error	t Stat	P-value	Lower 95%	Upper 95%	Lower 95.0%	Upper 95.0%
Intercept	1389.72222	41.40819949	33.561523	2.9E-16	1301.94078	1477.50366	1301.940781	1477.503664
INCENTIVE X1	623.333333	133.1827492	4.6802858	0.00025	340.998581	905.668085	340.9985814	905.6680853

We notice that the $SSE_r = 34{,}056.28$ and the $MSE_r = 2{,}128.52$. Compare these values to the ones found in the MINITAB printout on page 625 of the text. We now use the partial-F test statistic formula to calculate the desired test statistic.

$$F = \frac{(SSE_r - SSE_c)/(k - g)}{MSE_c} = \frac{(10{,}707.05)/2}{1{,}667.80} = 3.21$$

By fitting two regression models, a complete and a reduced model, the regression results can be combined in this manner to conduct a partial-F test. Compare this test statistic to the one found on page 625 of the *Statistics for Business and Economics* text. We refer you to the text for more information regarding the interpretation and use of this test statistic value.

Included in the data set disk with this manual is Example 12.4 of Chapter 12 from *Statistics for Business and Economics*. Use the procedures provided in the last example to practice conducting the partial-F test in Excel. Compare the results from the test to the ones found on pages 601 - 603 of the text.

Chapter 13
Methods for Quality Improvement

13.1 Introduction

Chapter 13 introduces the topic of quality improvement to the reader. The main topic covered in the text involves using scatter plots to create control charts that monitor the outcomes of a statistical process. These control charts specify upper and lower limits on the plot inside which the process is expected to stay. By using control charts, the user has a valid statistical tool that enables him/her to identify when a process is decreasing in quality.

Excel97 offers no data analysis or statistical tool that allows the user to create the control charts as studied in the text. As we saw in Chapter 2, however, Microsoft Excel® does allow the user to create scatter plots of data. If desired, the user could create a scatter plot of the appropriate variables used in the control chart within Excel and add, by hand, the control limits to the charts. While not ideal, the difficult task of plotting the observations could be done by Excel, and the rather easy task of drawing in the control limits could be done by the user.

We do not attempt to use this process here, but refer you to Example 2.3 of this manual in which a scatter plot was created within Excel.

Chapter 14
Time Series: Descriptive Analyses, Models, and Forecasting

14.1 Introduction

Chapter 14 of the *Statistics for Business and Economics* text introduces the reader to the topic of Time Series Analysis. Descriptive analyses, time series modeling, and time series forecasting are the three main time series areas covered by the text.

Excel offers a variety of methods that enable the user to work with time series data. Many, like simple data manipulation, scatter plots, and regression analysis, have been encountered in one of the previous chapters of this manual. We reference these topics when we look at how they can be applied to times series data. Excel also offers times series tools that are not covered in the *Statistics for Business and Economics* text. Moving averages, Seasonal Indexes, and Cyclical Effects are topics offered within Excel but not covered in the text. We refer the reader to a more comprehensive text on time series analysis for information concerning these topics.

One other Excel data analysis tool, exponential smoothing, will be introduced in this chapter and needs further discussion here. The exponential smoothing technique that Excel offers differs from the exponential smoothing technique discussed in the book. There are many smoothing techniques available and the generic 'exponential' label is misleading. For the purpose of this manual, we do not utilize the Excel exponential smoothing data analysis tool. We, instead, use simple formula manipulation of the time series data to get the desired exponentially smoothed values that are discussed in the text.

There are several time series topics, however, that Excel is unable to provide assistance with. Section 14.5 of the text introduces the Holt-Winters forecasting model, an extension of the exponential smoothing topic covered in Section 14.2. Excel provides no data analysis tool to handle this more complicated smoothing model. In addition, the topic of measuring forecast accuracy (Section 14.6) has no Excel equivalent data analysis tool. And, finally, the Durbin-Watson test for autocorrelation is also not covered in Excel.

We will use the chapter examples that are given in the text to illustrate the model building and testing methods discussed above. The following examples from *Statistics for Business and Economics* are solved with Microsoft Excel® in this chapter:

Excel Companion		Statistics for Business and Economics	
Example	Page	SBE Example	SBE Page
14.1	152	14.1	737
14.2	157	14.2	739
14.3	158	14.3	741
14.4	159	14.4	750

14.2 Descriptive Analyses: Index Numbers

Index numbers are the most common techniques for characterizing the change in a business or economic data series over time. These indexes can be constructed in a variety of manners. The text introduces the reader to the simple index, the simple composite index, and two different weighted composite indexes (Laspeyres and Paasche indexes). We examine how Excel can be used to generate these indexes in the examples that follow.

Example 14.1: We use Example 14.1 found on pages 737 - 738 in the *Statistics for Business and Economics* text.

One of the primary uses of index numbers is to characterize changes in stock prices over time. Stock market indexes have been constructed for many different types of companies and industries, and several composite indexes have been developed to characterize all stocks. These indexes are reported on a daily basis in the news media (e.g. Standard and Poor's 500 Stock Index and Dow Jones 65 Stocks Index).

Consider the monthly closing prices (i.e., closing prices on the last day of each month) given in Table 14.1 for four high-technology company stocks listed on the New York Stock Exchange between 1995 and 1996. To see how this type of stock fared, construct a simple composite index using January 1995 as the base period. Graph the index, and comment on its implications.

Solution:

Index values are found by taking the value of the series at some point in time and dividing by the value of the series during the base period and then multiplying this ratio by 100. Simple Composite indexes use totals from several different time series as the values in the index ratio. For this problem, we will use Excel to calculate the sum of the monthly closing prices of the listed stocks, and then use Excel to simply divide this sum by the sum found in the base year. The simple composite index will be found by multiplying this ratio by 100.

We use very basic data manipulation techniques within Excel to generate the desired indexes. We begin by **opening** the Excel97 file CX14_001 (or **importing** CXA14_01.prn). We will assume that the time series values are located in Columns B - F and Rows 2 - 25. The Column of totals should appear in Column G of the Excel worksheet. Note that Column H in the data sets has an abbreviated Month label. This column will be used to create the desired scatter plot. **Click** on the cell located in Row 2 Column I. **Enter** **=(G2/$G$2)*100** in the cell. Excel should return the value 100 in the I2 cell. **Copy** the I2 cell to the cells located in Column I Rows 3 - 25 (e.g., I3 - I25). Compare the results returned by Excel (see Table 14.2) to those found on page 737 of the text. (Note: It is important that the denominator of the formula listed above include the dollar signs as this tells Excel to use the G2 cell as the base level in all subsequent calculations).

Table 14.1

Year	Month	Bell Industries	Xerox	Digital Equipment	IBM	Total
1995	January	20.625	109.375	33.875	72.125	236
	February	20.875	110.875	33.625	75.25	240.625
	March	21.25	117.375	37.875	82.125	258.625
	April	20.125	123.375	46.125	94.625	284.25
	May	19.125	113.375	44.5	93	270
	June	21.375	117.25	40.75	96	275.375
	July	23.25	119.375	38.375	108.875	289.875
	August	21.125	120.875	41.75	103.375	287.125
	September	21.875	134.375	45.625	94.5	296.375
	October	21	129.625	54	97.25	301.875
	November	22.75	137.125	58.875	96.625	315.375
	December	22.5	137	64.125	91.375	315
1996	January	22.25	123.625	72.625	108.5	327
	February	21.75	130.25	72.625	122.625	347.25
	March	21.375	125.5	55	111.25	313.125
	April	22.125	146.5	59.875	107.75	336.25
	May	22	157.375	52.125	106.75	338.25
	June	16.75	160.5	45.125	99	321.375
	July	16.75	151.125	35.625	107.5	311
	August	16.75	164.625	38.625	114.375	334.375
	September	15.5	160.875	35.625	124.5	336.5
	October	16.75	139.125	29.5	129	314.375
	November	20.25	147	36.625	159.375	363.25
	December	21.375	157.875	36.25	151.5	367

Table 14.2

Year	Month	Bell Industries	Xerox	Digital Equipment	IBM	Total	*Index*
1995	January	20.625	109.375	33.875	72.125	236	100.00
	February	20.875	110.875	33.625	75.25	240.625	101.96
	March	21.25	117.375	37.875	82.125	258.625	109.59
	April	20.125	123.375	46.125	94.625	284.25	120.44
	May	19.125	113.375	44.5	93	270	114.41
	June	21.375	117.25	40.75	96	275.375	116.68
	July	23.25	119.375	38.375	108.875	289.875	122.83
	August	21.125	120.875	41.75	103.375	287.125	121.66
	September	21.875	134.375	45.625	94.5	296.375	125.58
	October	21	129.625	54	97.25	301.875	127.91
	November	22.75	137.125	58.875	96.625	315.375	133.63
	December	22.5	137	64.125	91.375	315	133.47
1996	January	22.25	123.625	72.625	108.5	327	138.56
	February	21.75	130.25	72.625	122.625	347.25	147.14
	March	21.375	125.5	55	111.25	313.125	132.68
	April	22.125	146.5	59.875	107.75	336.25	142.48
	May	22	157.375	52.125	106.75	338.25	143.33
	June	16.75	160.5	45.125	99	321.375	136.18
	July	16.75	151.125	35.625	107.5	311	131.78
	August	16.75	164.625	38.625	114.375	334.375	141.68
	September	15.5	160.875	35.625	124.5	336.5	142.58
	October	16.75	139.125	29.5	129	314.375	133.21
	November	20.25	147	36.625	159.375	363.25	153.92
	December	21.375	157.875	36.25	151.5	367	155.51

The scatter plot can be drawn in Excel using the Chart Wizard that was introduced in Chapter 2 of this manual. Click on the **Chart Wizard icon** that is located at the top of the Excel worksheet (see Figure 14.1). Highlight the **Line** Chart type and select the desired **Chart sub-type** that you desire. Click **Next**.

Figure 14.1

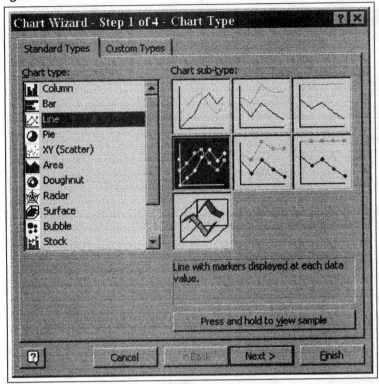

Enter the range of the data to be charted in the **Data Range** area of the menu (see Figure 14.2). Specify whether the data are listed in rows or **columns** by indicating the appropriate selection. Click Next.

The remaining Chart Wizard menus allow the user to customize the way the resulting line plot appears. We refer you to Chapter 2 of this manual to find a more thorough discussion of the options available within Excel. See Figure 14.3 for the plot created with Excel for the data of this example. Compare the Excel plot to the one found on page 738 of the *Statistics for Business and Economics* text.

Figure 14.2

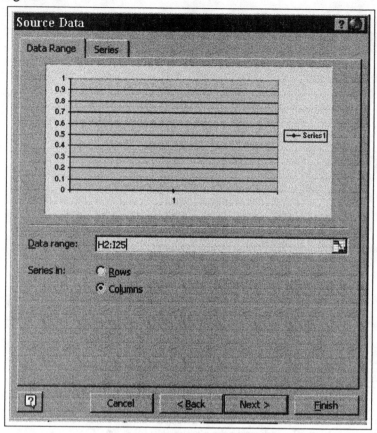

Figure 14.3

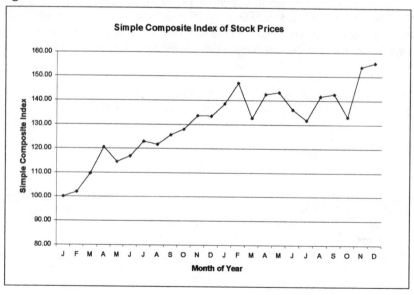

The simple composite index of Example 14.1 is found by summing the values of several times series and dividing by the sum from a base year. Each of the time series is given an equal weight in the simple composite index. Several different types of weighted composite indexes exist and the text discusses two such weighted composite indexes, Laspeyres and Paasche Indexes. We illustrate the Laspeyres Index below.

Example 14.2: We use Example 14.2 found on pages 739 - 740 in the *Statistics for Business and Economics* text.

The January prices for the four high technology company stocks are given in Table 14.3. Suppose that, in January 1995, an investor purchased the quantities shown in the table. [*Note:* Only January prices and quantities are used to simplify the example. The same methods can be applied to calculate the index for other months.] Calculate the Laspeyres index for the investor's portfolio of high-technology stocks using January 1995 as the base period.

Table 14.3

	Bell Industries	Xerox	Digital Equipment	IBM
Shares purchased	500	100	100	1000
January 1995 price	20.625	109.375	33.875	72.125
January 1996 price	22.25	123.625	72.625	108.5

Solution:

The first step in finding the Laspeyres indexes is to calculate the weighted price totals for each time period, using the January 1995 quantities as the weights. We begin by **opening** the Excel97 file CX14_002 (or importing CXA14_02.prn). We will assume that the weights are located in Columns B - E, Row 2 in the worksheet and the time series values are located in Columns B - E, Rows 3 - 4. **Click** on the cell located in Column F, Row 3. Enter
=$B$2*B3+$C$2*C3+$D$2*D3+$E$2*E3 in the cell. Make certain to use the "$" signs whenever you identify the cell locations of the weights. **Copy** the contents of Cell F3 to all the other cells in which weighted price totals are desired (e.g., Cell F4 in this example). Excel should return the weighted price totals shown below in Table 14.4.

The next step is to calculate the Laspeyres indexes using January 1995 as the base period. **Click** on the cell located in Column G, Row 3. Enter =(F3/$F$3)*100 in the cell. **Copy** the contents of Cell G3 to all the other cells in which the Laspeyres indexes are desired (e.g., Cell G4 in this example). Excel should return the Laspeyres indexes shown below in Table 14.4.

Table 14.4

	Bell Industries	Xerox	Digital Equipment	IBM	Weighted Totals	Lapeyres Index
Shares purchased	500	100	100	1000		
January 1995 price	20.625	109.375	33.875	72.125	96762.5	100
January 1996 price	22.25	123.625	72.625	108.5	139250	143.909056

Compare the results returned by Excel to those found on page 740 of the text.

As we have seen in the last example, the Laspeyres Index uses the quantities of the base period as the weights for all of the average and index values that are calculated. In some instances, it is preferred to use the quantities from the current time period as the weights in the index calculations. One method of achieving these indexes is to use the Paasche index. An example of the Paasche index follows.

Example 14.3: We use Example 14.3 found on pages 741 - 742 in the *Statistics for Business and Economics* text.

The January prices and volumes (actual quantities purchased) in thousands of shares for the four high-technology company stocks are shown for 1995 and 1996 in Table 14.5. Calculate and interpret the Paasche index, using January 1995 as the base period.

Table 14.5

	Bell Industries		Xerox		Digital Equipment		IBM	
	Price	Volume	Price	Volume	Price	Volume	Price	Volume
January 1995 price	20.625	261.9	109.375	8,723.8	33.875	24,206.0	72.125	52,484.7
January 1996 price	22.250	255.8	123.625	17,181.1	72.625	41,213.7	108.500	108,950.0

Solution:

The first step in finding the Paasche indexes is to calculate the weighted price totals for each time period, using the current time period quantities as the weights. We begin by **opening** the Excel97 file CX14_003 (or **importing** CXA14_03.prn). **Click** on the specified cell in the worksheet and enter:

For Q_{1996},P_{1996}: **=B4*C4+D4*E4+F4*G4+H4*I4** in cell A6
For Q_{1996},P_{1995}: **=B3*C4+D3*E4+F3*G4+H3*I4** in cell A7

For the Paasche index for 1996, enter **=(A6/A7)*100** in cell A9. Excel should return the Paasche index shown below in Table 14.6. Compare the results returned by Excel to those found on pages 741 - 742 of the text.

Table 14.6

Q_{1996},P_{1996}	16943925.00
Q_{1996},P_{1995}	11138591.53
Paasche Index	152.12

Using indexes is just one method of describing time series data. We turn our attention now towards the use of exponential smoothing as a method to describe time series data.

14.3 Exponential Smoothing

A second method of describing time series data involves averaging past and current data together. The goal of the averaging is to reduce the volatility that is inherent to any time series. Exponential smoothing is one type of averaging method that allows the user to select the amount of weight given to the past and to the present data. This weight, known as the smoothing constant, is selected to be a number between 0 and 1. The larger the value of the smoothing constant, the more weight is given to the most current data value from the time series. We demonstrate with the following example.

Example 14.4: We use Example 14.4 found on pages 750 - 751 in the *Statistics for Business and Economics* text.

Consider the IBM common stock price from January 1994 to December 1996, shown in Table 14.7. Create the exponentially smoothed series using $w = .5$, and plot both series.

Table 14.7

Month	IBM	Month	IBM	Month	IBM
Jan-94	56.500	Jan-95	72.125	Jan-96	108.500
Feb-94	52.875	Feb-95	75.250	Feb-96	122.625
Mar-94	54.625	Mar-95	82.125	Mar-96	111.250
Apr-94	57.500	Apr-95	94.625	Apr-96	107.750
May-94	63.000	May-95	93.000	May-96	106.750
Jun-94	58.750	Jun-95	96.000	Jun-96	99.000
Jul-94	61.875	Jul-95	108.875	Jul-96	107.500
Aug-94	68.500	Aug-95	103.375	Aug-96	114.375
Sep-94	69.625	Sep-95	94.500	Sep-96	124.500
Oct-94	74.500	Oct-95	97.250	Oct-96	129.000
Nov-94	70.750	Nov-95	96.625	Nov-96	159.375
Dec-94	73.500	Dec-95	91.375	Dec-96	151.500

Solution:

We begin by **opening** Excel97 file CX14_004 (or **importing** CXA14_04.prn). We will assume that the IBM stock prices appear in Column B, Rows 2 - 37 of the worksheet. To find the first exponentially smoothed value, enter =B2 in cell C2. To find the second exponentially smoothed value, we enter =.5*B3+(1-.5)*C2 in cell C3. We use the value of .5 in this equation because the smoothing constant for this problem is $w = .5$. Copy the formula of cell C3 to the cells C4 through C37 to obtain the rest of the exponentially smoothed values. Table 14.8 shows the values of the original time series as well as the exponentially smoothed values. Compare these values to the ones found on page 751 of the text.

Table 14.8

IBM	Smoothed	Month	IBM	Smoothed	Month	IBM	Smoothed
56.500	56.500	Jan-95	72.125	72.129059	Jan-96	108.500	101.39407
52.875	54.6875	Feb-95	75.250	73.689529	Feb-96	122.625	112.00954
54.625	54.65625	Mar-95	82.125	77.907265	Mar-96	111.250	111.62977
57.500	56.078125	Apr-95	94.625	86.266132	Apr-96	107.750	109.68988
63.000	59.539063	May-95	93.000	89.633066	May-96	106.750	108.21994
58.750	59.144531	Jun-95	96.000	92.816533	Jun-96	99.000	103.60997
61.875	60.509766	Jul-95	108.875	100.84577	Jul-96	107.500	105.55499
68.500	64.504883	Aug-95	103.375	102.11038	Aug-96	114.375	109.96499
69.625	67.064941	Sep-95	94.500	98.305192	Sep-96	124.500	117.2325
74.500	70.782471	Oct-95	97.250	97.777596	Oct-96	129.000	123.11625
70.750	70.766235	Nov-95	96.625	97.201298	Nov-96	159.375	141.24562
73.500	72.133118	Dec-95	91.375	94.288149	Dec-96	151.500	146.37281

Figure 14.4

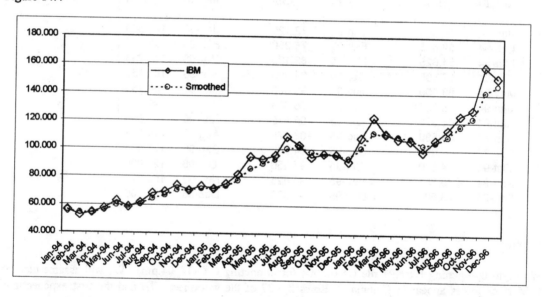

A plot of both the original time series the exponentially smoothed series is shown above in Figure 14.4. Compare this chart to the one shown on page 751 of the text. Note that any value of a smoothing constant can be used by changing the appropriate values in the formula used to calculate the exponentially smoothed values of the series. The exponentially smoothed values will change depending whether the constant places more weight on the current value or the past values of the time series.

Section 14.5 introduces the reader to a second type of smoothing process, the Holt-Winters smoothing model, as a method for forecasting values of a time series. The book gives the necessary formulas that can be used within Excel to find the Holt-Winters values. We leave this formula manipulation to the user. We recommend using the last example as a guide and substitute the Holt-Winters formulas for those used in the example. Use Example 14.6 from the text (page 758) to validate your work.

14.4 Using Regression to Model Time Series Data

Sections 14.7 and 14.8 introduce the reader to using regression models to model the linear trend and seasonal variation in time series data. The linear trend component can be modeled by using a measure of the time period as a quantitative variable in the regression. For example, the model $E(Y_t) = \beta_0 + \beta_1 t$ can be used to forecast the value of a time series at time period t. This model would assume that the time series values increase linearly over time.

While the linear model discussed above works in some applications, many time series data are affected by some sort of cyclical, or seasonal, influences. This cyclical variation can be modeled in regression using the qualitative variables discussed in Chapter 12. The seasonal component must be identified and explained using qualitative indicator variables. For example, the model
$E(Y_t) = \beta_0 + \beta_1 t + \beta_2 Q_1 + \beta_3 Q_2 + \beta_4 Q_3$ could be used to include both a linear trend (modeled with the quantitative time period variable, t) and a seasonal component (modeled with the three indicator variables Q_1, Q_2, and Q_3). The Q's in this model would be appropriate if the time series was influenced by some quarterly effect. For a monthly effect, the model would need to include eleven indicator variables.

We will not fit regression models to the time series data of chapter 14. We remind the user that Excel requires the data set to include all of the independent variables to be included in the regression model. The variables must be in adjacent columns of the Excel worksheet. We refer the user to Chapters 10 -12 of this manual to review how to fit regression models within Excel. The regression models fit will yield estimates to the values of the time series data of Chapter 14.

Chapter 15
Design of Experiments and Analysis of Variance

15.1 Introduction

Chapter 15 introduces the topics of design of experiments and analysis of variance (ANOVA) to the reader. The concept of the designed experiment is explained and the completely randomized and factorial designs are covered in the text. The goal of analysis of variance is to identify factors that contribute information to the response variable of interest. The combination of levels of the various factors are called treatments and the analysis of variance procedures discussed in the text attempt to detect differences in the mean response variable for the various treatments. Once detected, the text presents several methods of comparing the multiple means of the experiment. The final topic covered in the text relates the designed experiments of this chapter to the regression models of Chapters 10 - 12.

Excel97 offers two analysis of variance procedures that can be used for the completely randomized and factorial designs. These data analysis tools are very easy to implement. In addition, the regression data analysis tool that we examined in Chapters 10 - 12 can also be used to fit the ANOVA models of this chapter. Excel does not, however, offer a follow-up tool to compare treatment means that have been determined to differ. The Excel user must take the summary results from the two analyses and calculate the multiple comparison procedures by hand.

We will use the chapter examples that are given in the text to illustrate the model building and testing methods discussed above. The following examples from *Statistics for Business and Economics* are solved with Microsoft Excel® in this chapter:

Excel Companion		Statistics for Business and Economics	
Example	Page	SBE Example	SBE Page
15.1	164	15.3	810
15.2	166	15.6	834
15.3	170	15.8	848
15.4	173	15.9	849

15.2 The Completely Randomized Design

The goal of analysis of variance is to compare the mean responses of the various treatments in an experimental design, where the treatments are the combinations of the levels of all the factors involved in the design. The simplest of all experimental designs involves using a single factor to compare values of a response variable. Since there is only one factor in the design, the various levels of the factor are the treatments in the design. The goal is to compare the means of the response variable for those treatments. This experimental design is the completely randomized design and can be analyzed in Excel using the Anova: Single Factor data analysis tool. We illustrate with the following example.

Example 15.1: We use Example 15.3 found on pages 810 - 812 in the *Statistics for Business and Economics* text.

Suppose the United States Golf Association (USGA) wants to compare the mean distances associated with four different brands of golf balls when struck with a driver. A completely randomized design is employed, with Iron Byron, the USGA's robotic golfer, using a driver to hit a random sample of 10 balls of each brand in a random sequence. The distance is recorded for each hit, and the results are shown in Table 15.1, organized by brand.

a. Set up the test to compare the mean distances for the four brands. Use $\alpha = .10$.
b. Use Excel to obtain the test statistic and p-value. Interpret the results.

Table 15.1

BRAND A	BRAND B	BRAND C	BRAND D
251.2	263.2	269.7	251.6
245.1	262.9	263.2	248.6
248.0	265.0	277.5	249.4
251.1	254.5	267.4	242.0
260.5	264.3	270.5	246.5
250.0	257.0	265.5	251.3
253.9	262.8	270.7	261.8
244.6	264.4	272.9	249.0
254.6	260.6	275.6	247.1
248.8	255.9	266.5	245.9

Solution:

We begin by **opening** the Excel97 file CX15_003 (or **importing** CXA15_03.prn). Click on the **Tools** menu located at the top of the Excel worksheet. Select the **Data Analysis** option from within the Tools menu and highlight the **Anova: Single Factor** option (see Figure 15.1). Click **OK**.

Figure 15.1

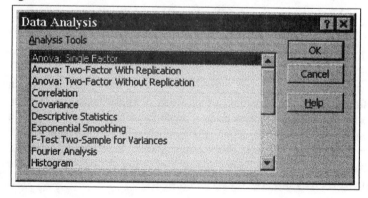

Either type or click the rows and columns where the input data is located and enter this information into the **Input Range** area of the Anova: Single Factor menu (see Figure 15.2). Select the manner in which the data is grouped **(Columns** or **Rows)** and give a level of significance in the **Alpha** cell of the menu (e.g., .10). Specify the location of the computed output by selecting either the **Output Range**, New Worksheet Ply, or New Workbook option, and entering the corresponding cell or name. Click **OK**.

Figure 15.2

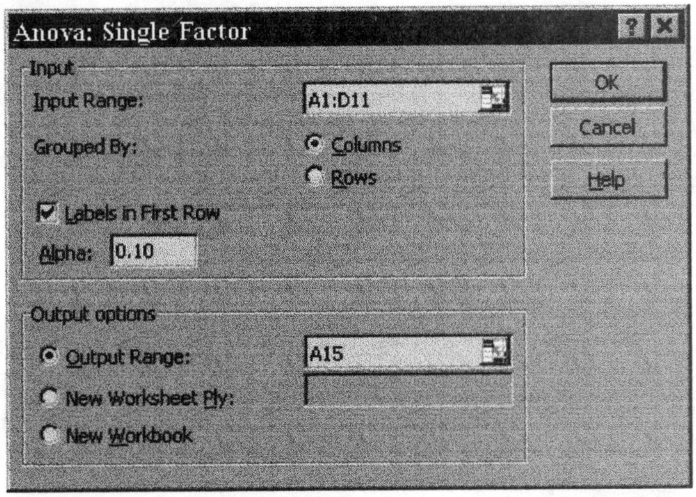

The ANOVA printout generated for the completely randomized design has two main components (see Table 15.2). The first component is a statistical summary of the various treatments in the analysis. For each of the four brands of balls, Excel gives some summary information concerning the distances achieved by each. This information will be more useful after studying the multiple comparison of means material in Section 15.3.

Table 15.2

Anova: Single Factor						
SUMMARY						
Groups	*Count*	*Sum*	*Average*	*Variance*		
BRAND A	10	2507.8	250.78	22.42177778		
BRAND B	10	2610.6	261.06	14.94711111		
BRAND C	10	2699.5	269.95	20.25833333		
BRAND D	10	2493.2	249.32	27.07288889		
ANOVA						
Source of Variation	*SS*	*df*	*MS*	*F*	*P-value*	*F crit*
Between Groups	2794.38875	3	931.4629167	43.98874592	3.97311E-12	2.242607877
Within Groups	762.301	36	21.17502778			
Total	3556.68975	39				

The second component is called the analysis of variance table and is where the pertinent testing information will be found. To test whether the mean distances of the four means differ, we use the test statistic and p-value found in the Brand row of the printout (labeled on the Excel printout as the Between Groups row). We see that the test statistic is F = 43.9887 and the p-value is p ≈ 0. Compare these values to the values found in the SAS printout found on page 811 of the text. We refer you to the text for further information regarding the interpretation of these values.

15.3 The Factorial Design

The next step in the experimental design process is to add a second factor to the design. One possible design that results is the factorial design. In Excel, the data analysis procedure that should be used is the Anova: Two-Factor With Replication procedure. This procedure allows both the factors to be analyzed as well as the interaction between them. We illustrate its use with the following example.

Example 15.2: We use Example 15.6 found on pages 834 - 837 in the *Statistics for Business and Economics* text.

Suppose the United States Golf Association (USGA) tests four different brands (A, B, C, D) of golf balls and two different clubs (driver, five-iron) in a completely randomized design. Each of the eight Brand-Club combinations (treatments) is randomly and independently assigned to four experimental units , each experimental unit consisting of a specific position in the sequence of hits by Iron Byron. The distance response is recorded for each of the 32 hits, and the results are shown in Table 15.3

a.   Use Excel to partition the Total Sum of Squares into the components necessary to analyze this 4x2 factorial experiment.

b.   Follow the steps for analyzing a two-factor factorial experiment and interpret the results of your analysis. Use α = .10 for the tests you conduct.

Table 15.3

| | | BRAND | | | |
		A	B	C	D
	DRIVER	226.4	238.3	240.5	219.8
	DRIVER	232.6	231.7	246.9	228.7
	DRIVER	234.0	227.7	240.3	232.9
CLUB	DRIVER	220.7	237.2	244.7	237.6
	FIVE-IRON	163.8	184.4	179.0	157.8
	FIVE-IRON	179.4	180.6	168.0	161.8
	FIVE-IRON	168.6	179.5	165.2	162.1
	FIVE-IRON	173.4	186.2	156.5	160.3

Solution:

We begin by **opening** the Excel97 file CX15_006 (or **importing** CXA15_06.prn). Click on the **Tools** menu located at the top of the Excel worksheet. Select the **Data Analysis** option from within the Tools menu and highlight the **Anova: Two Factor With Replication** option (see Figure 15.3). Click **OK**.

Figure 15.3

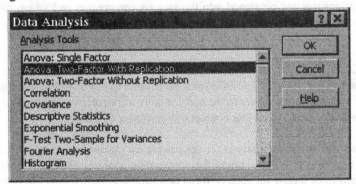

Either type or click the rows and columns where the input data is located and enter this information into the **Input Range** area of the Anova: Two Factor With Replication menu (see Figure 15.4). Include the labels for the columns and rows of the factor when inputting the data range. Note that each Brand of golf ball includes four rows of data for each of the two Clubs tested. Enter the number of rows (e.g., 4) in the **Rows per Sample** area of the menu. Give a level of significance in the **Alpha** cell of the menu (e.g., .10). Specify the location of the computed output by selecting either the **Output Range**, New Worksheet Ply, or New Workbook option, and entering the corresponding **cell** or name. Click **OK**.

Figure 15.4

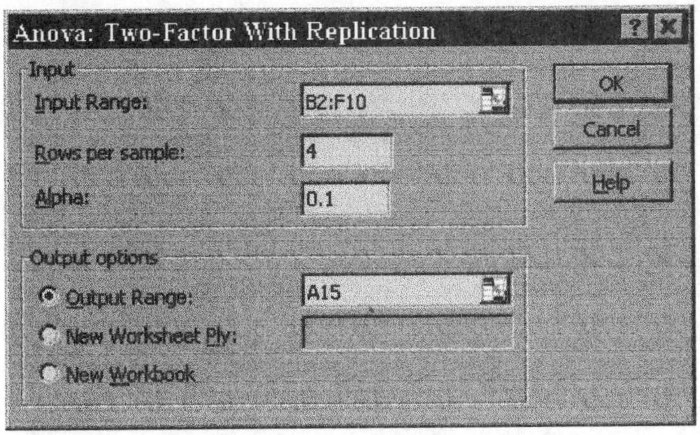

The ANOVA printout generated for the factorial design has two main components (see Table 15.4). The first component is a statistical summary of the various treatments in the analysis. For each of the eight Brand-Club treatments, Excel gives some summary information concerning the distances achieved by each. This information can be used when comparing individual treatment means similar to the methods used in Section 15.3.

The second component is the analysis of variance table and is where the pertinent testing information will be found. This is where the sums of squares are petitioned into the various components and where the interaction and individual factor test statistics and p-values are located. Compare this printout to the one found on page 835 of the text.

The first test of interest to the USGA is to determine if interaction exists between the Club and Brand factors in the experiment. We use the test statistic ($t = 7.452435$) and the p-value ($p = 0.001079$) found in the interaction row of the analysis of variance table. Refer to the text for more information concerning the interpretation of theses values and the follow-up analysis that is necessary for factorial designs.

We note here one drawback associated with the Excel analysis for the completely randomized and factorial designs in the analysis of variance experiments. Excel offers the appropriate analyses for determining when differences exist between the treatment means for each of these two experimental designs, but does not offer any method to determine where the specific differences exist. Both the SAS™ and MINITAB™ software packages offer options for conducting the multiple comparison procedures that enable the user to conduct the appropriate follow-up analysis for both the completely randomized and factorial designs. Consult Section 15.3 and the references at the end of the text for more information on this topic.

Table 15.4

Anova: Two-Factor With Replication					
SUMMARY	A	B	C	D	Total
DRIVER					
Count	4	4	4	4	16
Sum	913.7	934.9	972.4	919	3740
Average	228.425	233.725	243.1	229.75	233.75
Variance	37.429167	24.46917	10.53333	57.21667	61.07067
FIVE-IRON					
Count	4	4	4	4	16
Sum	685.2	730.7	668.7	642	2726.6
Average	171.3	182.675	167.175	160.5	170.4125
Variance	44.52	9.929167	86.1225	3.86	98.19183
Total					
Count	8	8	8	8	
Sum	1598.9	1665.6	1641.1	1561	
Average	199.8625	208.2	205.1375	195.125	
Variance	967.48268	759.3429	1688.454	1396.336	

ANOVA						
Source of Variation	SS	df	MS	F	P-value	F crit
Sample	32093.111	1	32093.11	936.7516	9.63E-21	2.927116
Columns	800.73625	3	266.9121	7.790779	0.00084	2.32739
Interaction	765.96125	3	255.3204	7.452435	0.001079	2.32739
Within	822.24	24	34.26			
Total	34482.049	31				

15.4 Using Regression Analysis for ANOVA

The analysis of variance designs of this chapter can be thought of as being composed of a quantitative dependent variable (called the response variable) and one (completely randomized design) or two (factorial design) qualitative independent variables (called factors). The regression modeling techniques discussed in Chapter 12 can easily be applied to the analysis of variance experiments of this chapter. The key to using regression analysis for ANOVA lies in defining the independent variables correctly.

15.4.1 Using Regression for the Completely Randomized Design

The completely randomized design is a single factor experiment that is composed of p levels for the one factor of interest. Regression analysis requires the user to define p-1 indicator variables to model the effects of these p levels on the value of the dependent variable. Refer to Section 12.6 of the text for more information concerning the use of indicator variables in regression modeling. We illustrate the use of regression analysis for the completely randomized design below.

Example 15.3: We use Example 15.8 found on pages 848 - 849 in the *Statistics for Business and Economics* text.

Refer to Example 15.1, in which we used ANOVA for a completely randomized design to test the hypothesis that the mean distances associated with four brands of golf balls were the same. Ten experimental units were randomly and independently assigned to each brand and the distance was recorded. The data are repeated in Table 15.5. Use a regression program to fit the equivalent regression model, and conduct the global F-test for the model's usefulness in predicting the response, *y*. Compare the test to that conducted in Example 15.1, and interpret the results use $\alpha = .10$.

Table 15.5

Distance Data for Golf Experiment Completely Randomized Design			
Brand A	Brand B	Brand C	Brand D
251.2	263.2	269.7	251.6
245.1	262.9	263.2	248.6
248	265	277.5	249.4
251.1	254.5	267.4	242
260.5	264.3	270.5	246.5
250	257	265.5	251.3
253.9	262.8	270.7	261.8
244.6	264.4	272.9	249
254.6	260.6	275.6	247.1
248.8	255.9	266.5	245.9
Means 250.78	261.06	269.95	249.32

Solution:

The first step necessary when solving this problem is to define the independent variables in such a manner that is useful to Excel. Refer to the Section 12.6 of the text for more information regarding the use of indicator variables in regression models. Since their are four levels of the variable Brand, we must define the following three indictor variables:

$$x_1 = \begin{cases} 1 \text{ if Brand A} \\ 0 \text{ if not} \end{cases} \qquad x_2 = \begin{cases} 1 \text{ if Brand B} \\ 0 \text{ if not} \end{cases} \qquad x_3 = \begin{cases} 1 \text{ if Brand C} \\ 0 \text{ if not} \end{cases}$$

The Excel data set used in the regression calculations is shown in Table 15.6.

The Regression data analysis tool in Excel can now be used to fit the following regression model:

$$E(y) = \beta_0 + \beta_1 x + \beta_2 x_2 + \beta_3 x_3$$

The goal is to generate the multiple regression model hypothesized above using Excel. The printout generated must include the standard regression output in order to conduct the desired global-F. Fortunately, the standard Excel regression output yields the needed information.

Table 15.6

x1	x2	x3	Y	x1	x2	x3	Y
1	0	0	251.2	0	0	1	269.7
1	0	0	245.1	0	0	1	263.2
1	0	0	248	0	0	1	277.5
1	0	0	251.1	0	0	1	267.4
1	0	0	260.5	0	0	1	270.5
1	0	0	250	0	0	1	265.5
1	0	0	253.9	0	0	1	270.7
1	0	0	244.6	0	0	1	272.9
1	0	0	254.6	0	0	1	275.6
1	0	0	248.8	0	0	1	266.5
0	1	0	263.2	0	0	0	251.6
0	1	0	262.9	0	0	0	248.6
0	1	0	265	0	0	0	249.4
0	1	0	254.5	0	0	0	242
0	1	0	264.3	0	0	0	246.5
0	1	0	257	0	0	0	251.3
0	1	0	262.8	0	0	0	261.8
0	1	0	264.4	0	0	0	249
0	1	0	260.6	0	0	0	247.1
0	1	0	255.9	0	0	0	245.9

We begin by **opening** Excel97 file CX15_008 (or **importing** CXA15_08.prn). At the main menu, click on
the **Tools** menu located at the top of the Excel worksheet. Select the **Data Analysis** option from within the
Tools menu and highlight the **Regression** option from the choices given in the Data Analysis menu (see
Figure 15.5). Click **OK**.

Figure 15.5

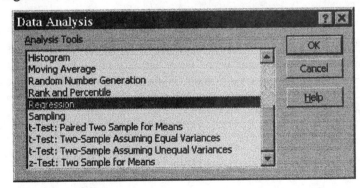

Inside the Regression menu, enter the dependent variable (Y) into the Input Y Range by either **typing** or **clicking on the cells** where the dependent variable is located (see Figure 15.6). **Repeat** this procedure for the independent variables (X_1, X_2, and X_3). We note here that the variable columns for X_1, X_2, and X_3 must be adjacent to one another in the data set when entering these variables into the Input X range in this menu. The only other item that needs to be entered is the choice for where the output will be generated at in the Output Options section of the Regression menu. **Check** either the Output Range, New Worksheet Ply, or New Workbook and **specify** the location or name in the space provided in the menu. Click **OK**.

Figure 15.6

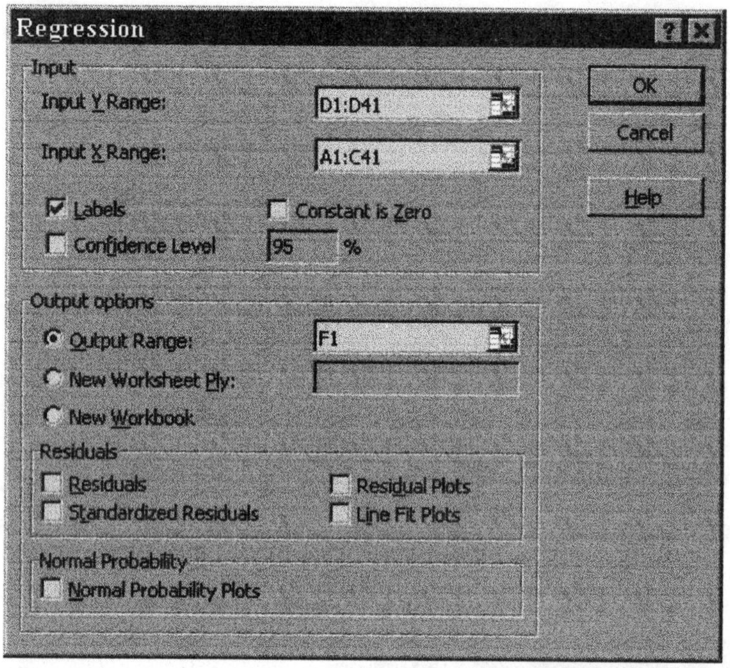

Excel generates the output shown in Table 15.7 below. Compare this output to the MINITAB output shown on page 848 of the text. In order to determine whether the mean distances of the four golf ball brands differ, we use the test statistic and p-value shown on the printout for the global-F test. The printout shows that $F = 43.98874592$ and $p \approx 0$. We refer you to the text for more detailed information regarding the interpretations and conclusions that should be made for these values.

Table 15.7

SUMMARY OUTPUT

Regression Statistics	
Multiple R	0.886380964
R Square	0.785671213
Adjusted R Square	0.767810481
Standard Error	4.601633164
Observations	40

ANOVA

	df	SS	MS	F	Significance F
Regression	3	2794.38875	931.4629167	43.98874592	3.97311E-12
Residual	36	762.301	21.17502778		
Total	39	3556.68975			

	Coefficients	Standard Error	t Stat	P-value	Lower 95%	Upper 95%	Lower 95.0%	Upper 95.0%
Intercept	249.32	1.455164176	171.3346193	5.08704E-54	246.3687942	252.2712058	246.3687942	252.2712058
x1	1.46	2.057912913	0.70945665	0.482611112	-2.713635337	5.633635337	-2.713635337	5.633635337
x2	11.74	2.057912913	5.704808949	1.72403E-06	7.566364663	15.91363534	7.566364663	15.91363534
x3	20.63	2.057912913	10.02471964	5.81562E-12	16.45636466	24.80363534	16.45636466	24.80363534

15.4.2 Using Regression for the Factorial Design

The factorial design is a two factor experiment that is composed of a levels for one factor and b levels for the second factor of interest. The factorial design also allows for interaction between the ab levels of the treatments of the experiment. Regression analysis requires the user to define many different indicator variables to model the various effects of the factorial. Refer to Section 12.6 of the text for more information concerning the use of indicator variables in regression modeling. We illustrate the use of regression analysis for the factorial design below.

Example 15.4: We use Example 15.9 found on pages 849 - 852 in the *Statistics for Business and Economics* text.

Refer to Example 15.2, in which we employed a factorial experiment in a completely randomized design to evaluate the effects of two factors, Brand of golf ball and Club utilized, on mean distance. Four brands and two clubs were utilized, and the 4x2 factorial was replicated four times. the data are repeated in Table 15.8.

a.   Write a regression model to represent the factorial experiment.

b.   Use Excel to fit the regression model. Conduct an analysis similar to that employed in the ANOVA of Example 15.2.

Table 15.8

Distance Data for Second Facorial Golf Experiment				
		Brand		
	A	B	C	D
Driver	226.4	238.3	240.5	219.8
	232.6	231.7	246.9	228.7
	234	227.7	240.3	232.9
	220.7	237.2	244.7	237.6
Five-Iron	163.8	184.4	179	157.8
	179.4	180.6	168	161.8
	168.6	179.5	165.2	162.1
	173.4	186.2	156.5	160.3

Solution:

The first step necessary when solving this problem is to define the independent variables in such a manner that is useful to Excel. Refer to the Section 12.6 of the text for more information regarding the use of indicator variables in regression models. Since their are four levels of the variable Brand, we must define the following three indictor variables:

$$x_1 = \begin{cases} 1 \text{ if Brand A} \\ 0 \text{ if not} \end{cases} \qquad x_2 = \begin{cases} 1 \text{ if Brand B} \\ 0 \text{ if not} \end{cases} \qquad x_3 = \begin{cases} 1 \text{ if Brand C} \\ 0 \text{ if not} \end{cases}$$

In addition, another indicator variable, x_4, must be defined to indicate which of the two clubs is being used by the testing machine. We define x_4 as follows:

$$x_4 = \begin{cases} 1 \text{ if Driver} \\ 0 \text{ if Five-Iron} \end{cases}$$

The factorial design also allows for the interaction between the golf ball brand and the club selection. The interaction variables $x_1 x_4$, $x_2 x_4$, and $x_3 x_4$ must also be defined in the Excel data set. All of these indicator variables must be located in adjacent columns in the Excel worksheet in order to fit a regression model to the data. Table 15.9 shows the columns and values necessary to fit a regression model in Excel.

The goal of this problem is to duplicate the ANOVA analysis of Example 15.2 using regression models. There are two regression models that must be fit in order to accomplish this goal. The first model, the complete model, will contain all the variables discussed above and shown in Table 15.9. The second model, the reduced model, will contain the indicator variables for both the Brand and Club factors, but will not include the interaction components in the model. This will allow a test of the interaction component to be conducted using the partial F-test of Section 12.5. Please refer to Section 12.5 of the text for more details regarding this testing procedure.

Table 15.9

X_1	X_2	X_3	X_4	X_1X_4	X_2X_4	X_3X_4	Y
1	0	0	1	1	0	0	226.4
1	0	0	1	1	0	0	232.6
1	0	0	1	1	0	0	234
1	0	0	1	1	0	0	220.7
1	0	0	0	0	0	0	163.8
1	0	0	0	0	0	0	179.4
1	0	0	0	0	0	0	168.6
1	0	0	0	0	0	0	173.4
0	1	0	1	0	1	0	238.3
0	1	0	1	0	1	0	231.7
0	1	0	1	0	1	0	227.7
0	1	0	1	0	1	0	237.2
0	1	0	0	0	0	0	184.4
0	1	0	0	0	0	0	180.6
0	1	0	0	0	0	0	179.5
0	1	0	0	0	0	0	186.2
0	0	1	1	0	0	1	240.5
0	0	1	1	0	0	1	246.9
0	0	1	1	0	0	1	240.3
0	0	1	1	0	0	1	244.7
0	0	1	0	0	0	0	179
0	0	1	0	0	0	0	168
0	0	1	0	0	0	0	165.2
0	0	1	0	0	0	0	156.5
0	0	0	1	0	0	0	219.8
0	0	0	1	0	0	0	228.7
0	0	0	1	0	0	0	232.9
0	0	0	1	0	0	0	237.6
0	0	0	0	0	0	0	157.8
0	0	0	0	0	0	0	161.8
0	0	0	0	0	0	0	162.1
0	0	0	0	0	0	0	160.3

The models we will be fitting are:

Complete Model: $E(y) = \beta_0 + \beta_1 x + \beta_2 x_2 + \beta_3 x_3 + \beta_4 x_4 + \beta_5 x_1 x_4 + \beta_6 x_2 x_4 + \beta_7 x_3 x_4$

Reduced Model: $E(y) = \beta_0 + \beta_1 x + \beta_2 x_2 + \beta_3 x_3 + \beta_4 x_4$

We begin by fitting the complete model above. **Open** Excel97 file CX15_008 (or **import** CXA15_08.prn).
At the main menu, click on the **Tools** menu located at the top of the Excel worksheet. Select the **Data Analysis** option from within the Tools menu and highlight the **Regression** option from the choices given in the Data Analysis menu (see Figure 15.7). Click **OK**.

Figure 15.7

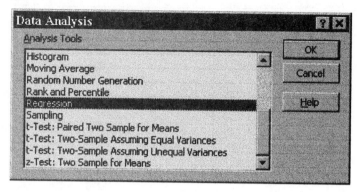

Inside the Regression menu, enter the dependent variable (Y) into the Input Y Range by either **typing** or **clicking on the cells** where the dependent variable is located (see Figure 15.8). **Repeat** this procedure for the independent variables (all the x's and the interaction terms). The only other item that needs to be entered is the choice for where the output will be generated at in the Output Options section of the Regression menu. **Check** either the Output Range, New Worksheet Ply, or New Workbook and **specify** the location or name in the space provided in the menu. Click **OK**.

Figure 15.8

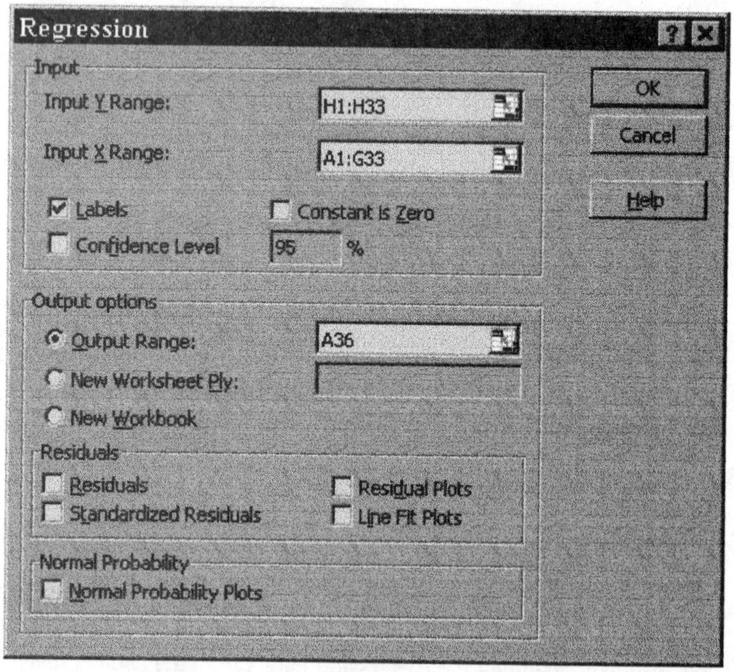

Excel generates the output shown in Table 15.10 below. Compare this output to the SAS output shown on page 850 of the text. In order to conduct the global F-test for the experiment, we use the F statistic and p-value found on the regression line of the ANOVA table. The printout shows that F = 140.354469 and p $\approx$ 0. We refer you to the text for more detailed information regarding the interpretations and conclusions that should be made for these values.

We should note here that the estimated coefficients of this printout and the one shown on page 850 of the text do not match. This is because the indicator variables were defined differently when the printouts were generated. The indicator variables can be defined in any fashion as the tests of interest do not depend on the definition used. The values from the printout that are needed in the testing, the global F-statistic and the p-value, are the same on both printouts.

Table 15.10

SUMMARY OUTPUT

Regression Statistics	
Multiple R	0.98800534
R Square	0.97615455
Adjusted R Square	0.96919963
Standard Error	5.85320425
Observations	32

ANOVA

	df	SS	MS	F	Sign. F
Regression	7	33659.8088	4808.54411	140.354469	6.72397E-18
Residual	24	822.24	34.26		
Total	31	34482.0488			

	Coefficients	Standard Error	t Stat	P-value	Lower 95%	Upper 95%	Lower 95.0%	Upper 95.0%
Intercept	160.5	2.926602125	54.841756	9.8E-27	154.459791	166.540209	154.4597913	166.5402087
X1	10.8	4.138840417	2.6094265	0.01537	2.25785497	19.342145	2.257854974	19.34214503
X2	22.175	4.138840417	5.3577809	1.7E-05	13.632855	30.717145	13.63285497	30.71714503
X3	6.675	4.138840417	1.6127706	0.11987	-1.867145	15.217145	-1.86714503	15.21714503
X4	69.25	4.138840417	16.73174	9.8E-15	60.707855	77.792145	60.70785497	77.79214503
X1X4	-12.125	5.853204251	-2.0715149	0.04923	-24.205417	-0.0445827	-24.2054173	-0.044582653
X2X4	-18.2	5.853204251	-3.109408	0.00478	-30.280417	-6.1195827	-30.2804173	-6.119582653
X3X4	6.675	5.853204251	1.140401	0.26537	-5.4054173	18.7554173	-5.40541735	18.75541735

The second part of the analysis for this factorial design is to test the interaction component of the complete model to determine if it is useful in modeling the distance variable. This can be done using the partial F-test of Section 12.5. We now use Excel to fit the reduced model listed above to the data.

We continue using the same data set as was used to fit the complete model, but now specify only a portion of the variables to use as independent variables in the regression model. At the main menu, click on the **Tools** menu located at the top of the Excel worksheet. Select the **Data Analysis** option from within the Tools menu and highlight the **Regression** option from the choices given in the Data Analysis menu (see Figure 15.9). Click **OK**.

Figure 15.9

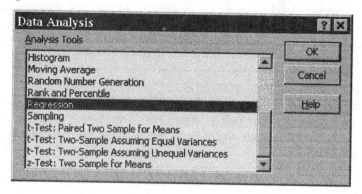

Inside the Regression menu, enter the dependent variable (Y) into the Input Y Range by either **typing or clicking on the cells** where the dependent variable is located (see Figure 15.10). **Repeat** this procedure for the independent variables (just x_1, x_2, x_3, and x_4). The only other item that needs to be entered is the choice for where the output will be generated at in the Output Options section of the Regression menu. **Check** either the Output Range, New Worksheet Ply, or New Workbook and **specify** the location or name in the space provided in the menu. Click **OK**.

Figure 15.10

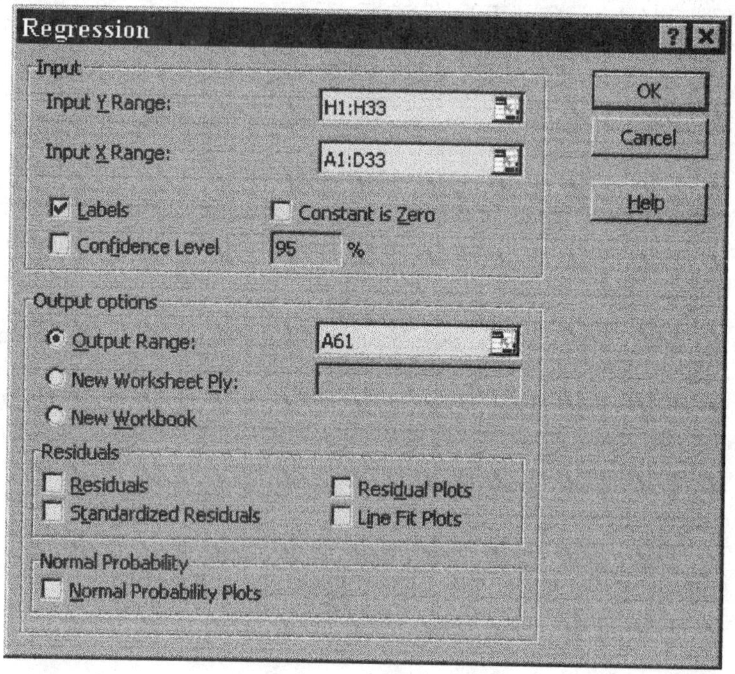

Excel generates the output shown in Table 15.11 below. Compare this output to the SAS output shown on page 851 of the text. In order to conduct the partial F-test for the experiment, we use the Sum of Squared Error and Mean Square Error values found on the printouts for both the complete and reduced models. We refer you to Section 12.5 of the text for more detailed information regarding the partial F-test and the corresponding interpretations and conclusions that should be made for this test.

Table 15.11

SUMMARY OUTPUT

Regression Statistics	
Multiple R	0.97669914
R Square	0.95394122
Adjusted R Square	0.94711769
Standard Error	7.66956769
Observations	32

ANOVA

	df	SS	MS	F	Sign. F
Regression	4	32693.8475	8223.46188	139.8018486	1.25041E-17
Residual	27	1588.20125	58.8222685		
Total	31	34482.0488			

	Coefficients	Standard Error	t Stat	P-value	Lower 95%	Upper 95%	Lower 95.0%	Upper 95.0%
Intercept	163.45625	3.03166282	53.916369	5E-29	157.235796	169.676704	157.2357959	169.6767041
X1	4.7375	3.834783844	1.2354021	0.22732	-3.1308212	12.6058212	-3.13082124	12.60582124
X2	13.075	3.834783844	3.4095794	0.00206	5.20667876	20.9433212	5.206678755	20.94332124
X3	10.0125	3.834783844	2.6109685	0.01456	2.14417876	17.8808212	2.144178755	17.88082124
X4	63.3375	2.71160166	23.357966	1.9E-19	57.7737567	68.9012433	57.77375669	68.90124331

The regression modeling procedures within Excel can be used to accommodate any of the ANOVA designs discussed in the text. The user must first identify the factors of interest in the design and define the appropriate indicator variables to use in the regression model. The user must also consider whether the interaction between factors is a needed component in the model. These considerations should allow the regression data analysis tool within Excel to provide the necessary printouts to conduct the various statistical tests presented in this chapter.

Chapter 16
Nonparametric Statistics

16.1 Introduction

Chapter 16 introduces the topic of nonparametric data analysis to the reader. The nonparametric analyses are alternative procedures to the parametric procedures of Chapters 8 - 12, and 15. No Microsoft Excel® procedures are available to work with these nonparametric procedures.

Chapter 17
The Chi-Square Test and the Analysis of Contingency Tables

17.1 Introduction

Chapter 17 introduces the topic of categorical data analysis to the reader. There are two main types of analyses presented; the one-way and two-way studies. Both studies utilize the chi-square sampling distribution. While Microsoft Excel® does offer a chi-square statistical function, it has limited use when working with the studies of Chapter 17. Excel does not offer any other data analysis tools for working with categorical data.

Chapter 18
Decision Analysis

18.1 Introduction

Chapter 18 introduces the topic of decision analysis to the reader. No data analysis using Microsoft Excel®
is necessary in Chapter 18.